1-Team Names

ACROSS

2 Baseball team from Houston

7 National League team from Atlanta

9 American League team from Detroit

11 National League team from Arizona

14 National League team from Philadelphia

16 National League team from New York

17 American League team from Texas

19 National League team from Chicago

20 National League team from Los Angeles

21 Baseball team from San Francisco

DOWN

1 American League team from Baltimore

3 American League team from Minnesota

4 American League team from Seattle

5 Baseball team from St. Louis

6 Baseball team from Chicago

8 American League team from Cleveland

10 MLB team from Boston: Boston ___ Sox

12 American League team from Oakland

13 National League team from Milwaukee

15 Baseball team from New York

18 American League team from Kansas City

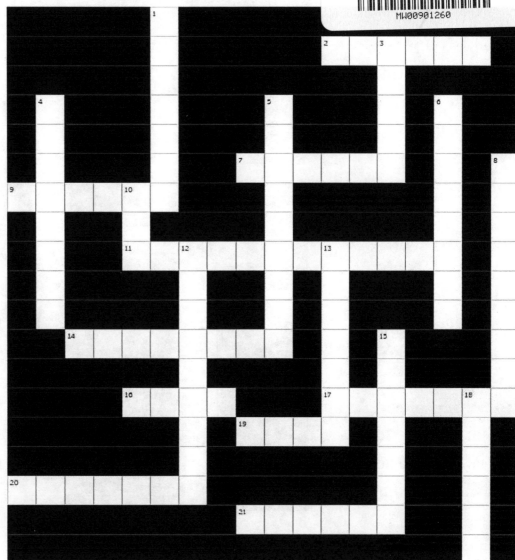

2- Player Names

ACROSS

4 Hall of Fame Yankees outfielder known as "The Sultan of Swat"

6 Cardinals first baseman with 3 MVP Awards: Albert ___

7 Red Sox left fielder who broke the "Curse of the Bambino": Manny ___

8 Legendary Giants center fielder with a famous "Catch": Willie ___

10 Dodgers pitcher with 7 no-hitters: ___ Ryan

12 Hall of Fame pitcher known as "The Rocket": Roger ___

16 Legendary Red Sox outfielder with 18 All-Star selections: Ted ___

17 Mets pitcher with three Cy Young Awards: Tom ___

18 Athletics outfielder known as "Mr. October": Reggie ___

DOWN

1 Home run king with 762 career homers: Barry ___

2 Yankees shortstop known as "The Captain": Derek ___

3 Hall of Fame second baseman with 3,000 hits: Roberto ___

4 Orioles shortstop known as "The Iron Man" for his consecutive games streak: Cal ___ Jr.

5 Braves third baseman with 755 career home runs: Hank ___

9 Tigers outfielder known as "Mr. Tiger"

11 Hall of Fame pitcher nicknamed "Big Unit": Randy ___

13 Braves pitcher with 355 career wins: Greg ___

14 Hall of Fame pitcher known for his "Forkball": Bruce ___

15 Yankees closer with a record 652 career saves: Mariano ___

- THE ULTIMATE -

BASEBALL CROSSWORD PUZZLES

LARGE PRINT

THIS BOOK BELONGS TO:

OMAMOVA
-PUBLISHING-

3- Ballpark Names

ACROSS

4 MLB stadium in Houston: _ _ _ Maid Park

6 MLB ballpark in Arlington, Texas: _ _ _ Life Field

8 Ballpark in Washington, D.C.: _ _ _ Park

9 Home of an MLB team in New York: _ _ _ Stadium

11 Home of the San Francisco Giants: _ _ _ Park

12 Ballpark located in St. Louis: _ _ _ Stadium

15 Baseball park in Chicago, home to the Cubs: _ _ _ Field

16 Home of the Los Angeles: _ _ _ Stadium

18 Home of the Cincinnati Reds: Great _ _ _ Ball Park

19 Ballpark in Denver, home to the Rockies: _ _ _ Field

DOWN

1 Baseball stadium in Atlanta: _ _ _ Park

2 Former home of the New York Mets: _ _ _ Stadium

3 Historic ballpark in Boston: _ _ _ Park

5 Ballpark located in Cleveland: _ _ _ Field

6 Home of the Chicago White Sox: _ _ _ Rate Field

7 Home of the Toronto Blue Jays: _ _ _ Centre

10 Stadium in Milwaukee, home of the Brewers: American _ _ _ Field

13 Home of the Philadelphia Phillies: _ _ _ Bank Park

14 Baseball stadium in Anaheim: _ _ _ Stadium

17 Stadium in Pittsburgh, known for its yellow bridge: _ _ _ Park

4- Batting Terms

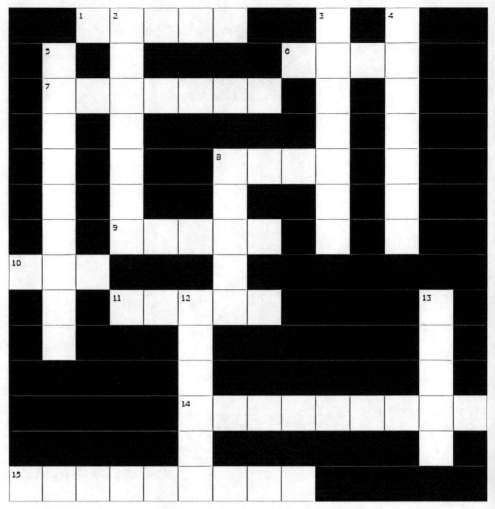

ACROSS

1 A hit that lands softly in the infield: ___ Single

6 A hit that lands just outside the foul lines: ___ Ball

7 A hit that is caught by an outfielder after a long run: ___ Catch

8 A hit that lands just inside the foul lines: ___ Ball

9 A hit that drops just behind the infielders: ___ Leaguer

10 A hit that goes between outfielders: ___ Shot

11 A hit that is struck with such force that it leaves the ballpark very quickly: ___ Shot

14 A pitch that is hit directly into the ground

15 A swing and miss by the batter

DOWN

2 A pitch that is hit sharply but directly at a fielder

3 A hit that goes over the outfield fence

4 A hit that bounces just over the infielders' heads and into the outfield

5 A pitch that brushes against the batter's body but does not hit them

8 A hit that goes off the end of the bat and typically results in a weakly hit ball

12 A hit that rolls slowly towards an infielder: Infield ___

13 A pitch that is hit high into the air but not far

5- Pitching Terms

ACROSS

2 A pitch aimed at the batter's head to disrupt their timing

4 A pitch with a sharp downward break

7 A pitch that is thrown intentionally outside the strike zone to entice the batter to swing

8 A pitch that is thrown to the inside of the plate, often to brush back the batter: Inside ___

10 A pitch with a very slow speed and high arc

12 A pitch that is thrown with the intent of hitting the batter

14 A pitch thrown with a sidearm motion, causing it to move horizontally

15 A pitch that is thrown with a tight, spinning motion, resulting in sharp movement

16 A pitch that appears to be headed for the strike zone but then moves out of the way: ___ Ball

DOWN

1 A pitch that starts inside and moves back over the plate: ___ Slider

3 A pitch that breaks sharply down and away from the batter

5 A pitch that is thrown with a spinning motion that causes it to drop sharply as it approaches the plate

6 A pitch that is thrown high above the strike zone

9 A pitch that breaks in toward the batter's body

11 A pitch that is thrown with maximum speed

13 A pitch that is thrown with a high arc and minimal rotation

14 A pitch with a sharp, late break

6- Fielding Terms

ACROSS

4 The area of the field where the infielders play

5 The area of the field where outfielders play

6 A defensive player positioned behind home plate

7 A defensive player positioned between first and second base: Second ___

10 The act of a fielder throwing the ball to another player to record an out: ___'s Assist

12 A defensive player positioned between second and third base

14 The act of a fielder catching a ball before it touches the ground

15 A catch made by a fielder while sliding towards the ground: ___ Catch

16 A catch made by a fielder in the outfield while running towards the infield: ___ Catch

17 A play in which two defensive players cooperate to retire a baserunner: ___ Play

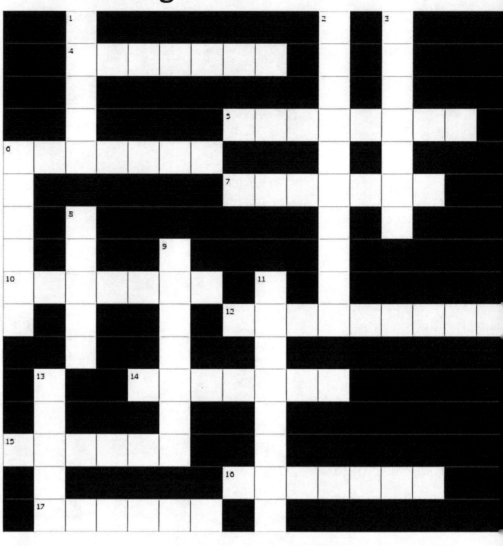

DOWN

1 The defensive position located to the right of the center fielder: ___ Field

2 A defensive player stationed in the outfield

3 A defensive player positioned between the shortstop and first base: First ___

6 The act of a fielder stopping a ball from rolling into the outfield

8 The defensive position located to the left of the center fielder: Left ___

9 A catch made by a fielder while leaping into the air: ___ Catch

11 A play in which a defensive player quickly throws the ball to retire a baserunner

13 A defensive player positioned between the pitcher and third base: ___ Baseman

7- Base Running

ACROSS

2 A play in which a baserunner advances to the next base without the ball being hit: _ _ _ Base

3 A play in which a baserunner is caught between two bases and tagged out

4 The act of a baserunner quickly returning to a previous base to avoid being tagged out

7 The area where baserunners wait before attempting to advance

9 The act of a baserunner attempting to steal a base while the pitcher is delivering the ball to the batter: _ _ _ Steal

11 The area where baserunners stand to await their turn to bat: On Deck _ _ _

12 The act of a baserunner running from home plate to first base on a ground ball: _ _ _ to First

13 The act of a baserunner quickly advancing to the next base without stopping: Taking _ _ _ Base

DOWN

1 The area on the field where a baserunner must touch to score a run: _ _ _ Plate

2 A play in which a baserunner advances to the next base without the ball being hit

4 A baserunner who is not occupying a base

5 The act of a baserunner touching a base to be safe from being tagged out: _ _ _ Base

6 The act of a baserunner waiting on a base for a signal from the coach or batter

8 A play in which a baserunner touches all four bases and scores a run

10 A play in which a baserunner advances to the next base due to a mistake by the defense

8- World Series

ACROSS

6 The last team to win three consecutive World Series championships

8 The month in which the World Series is usually played

9 The team that has appeared in the most World Series without winning

11 The first team to win the World Series: Boston _ _ _

DOWN

1 The baseball term for a hit that clears the outfield fence

2 The trophy awarded to the World Series winner: _ _ _'s Trophy

3 The term for the team that does not win the World Series

4 The city that hosted the first World Series

5 The stadium where the first World Series was played in 1903: _ _ _ Avenue Grounds

7 The championship series in Major League Baseball: _ _ _ Series

10 The number of games typically played in a World Series

12 The number of outs in a regulation inning of baseball

9- All-Stars

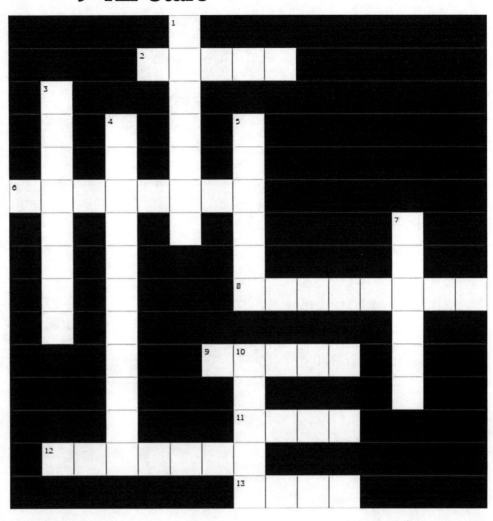

ACROSS

2 This player was named the All-Star Game MVP in two consecutive years: Mike _ _ _

6 This pitcher holds the record for the most strikeouts in All-Star Game history: Don _ _ _

8 He won the All-Star Game MVP award in 2017: _ _ _ Cano

9 The MLB player who won the first All-Star Game MVP award in 1962: _ _ _ Wills

11 He hit the first home run in All-Star Game history.

12 The city that hosted the first-ever MLB All-Star Game

13 The number of innings typically played in an All-Star Game.

DOWN

1 The MLB player who won the All-Star Game MVP award in 2018: Alex _ _ _

3 The MLB player who won the All-Star Game MVP award in 2021: Vladimir _ _ _ Jr.

4 This player holds the record for the most hits in All-Star Game history: Carl _ _ _

5 He won the All-Star Game MVP award in 2019

7 The MLB player who holds the record for the most home runs in All-Star Game history: Stan _ _ _

10 He holds the record for the most All-Star Game appearances: Hank _ _ _

10- Hall of Fame

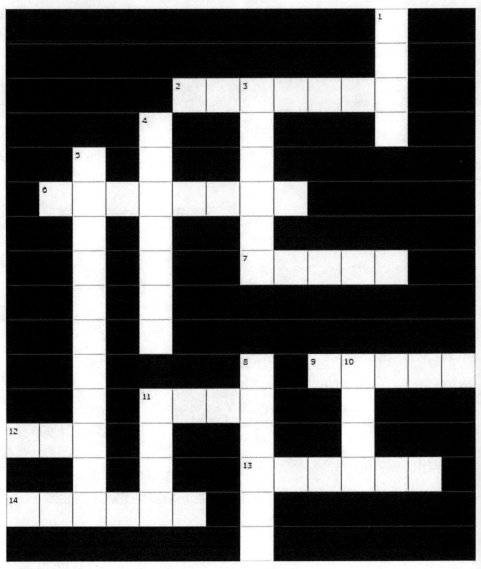

ACROSS

2 The player who was the first African American pitcher inducted into the Baseball Hall of Fame: _ _ _ Paige

6 The first African American player inducted into the Baseball Hall of Fame: Jackie _ _ _

7 The player with the most career home runs who is not in the Baseball Hall of Fame

9 The former Commissioner of Baseball who was inducted into the Hall of Fame in 1970: Ford _ _ _

11 The number of years a player must be retired to be eligible for induction into the Baseball Hall of Fame

12 The number of players inducted into the Baseball Hall of Fame in 2023

13 The only player to be unanimously elected to the Baseball Hall of Fame

14 The first woman elected to the Baseball Hall of Fame: Effa _ _ _

DOWN

1 The Baseball Hall of Fame's annual induction ceremony takes place in this month

3 The first player inducted into the Baseball Hall of Fame

4 The organization responsible for electing players to the Baseball Hall of Fame: Baseball _ _ _' Association of America (BBWAA)

5 The Baseball Hall of Fame is located in this town in New York

8 The player known as "The Iron Horse" who was inducted into the Baseball Hall of Fame in 1939: Lou _ _ _

10 The player with the most career hits who is not in the Baseball Hall of Fame: Pete _ _ _

11 The number of players inducted into the Baseball Hall of Fame in its inaugural class

11- Home Runs

ACROSS

3 Game-winning home run

4 Nickname for home run

6 Opposite of a home run (one base)

8 Home run without leaving field

10 Home run landing in water

11 Most career home runs: Barry _ _ _

12 Part of the field a home run goes over

13 Barely clears fence home run: Fence _ _ _

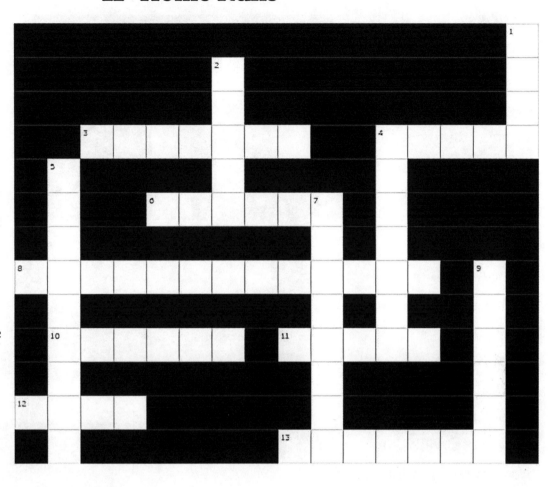

DOWN

1 Bases scored on home run

2 Negative fan reaction to opposing team's home run

4 Pitcher allowing a home run

5 Bases loaded home run

7 Feeling of hitting a home run

9 Player who hits a home run

12- Strikeouts

ACROSS

3 The pitcher with the most career strikeouts for a left-handed pitcher: Randy _ _ _

6 The record-holder for the most career strikeouts in Major League Baseball

8 The term for a batter striking out four times in a game: _ _ _ Sombrero

10 Pitching stat associated with strikeouts, walks, and hits allowed per inning

11 The number of consecutive strikeouts needed by a pitcher to tie the MLB record

12 The pitcher who holds the record for the most strikeouts in a single postseason game: Bob _ _ _

13 One of the 3 pitchers who holds the MLB record for the most strikeouts in a single game, with 20 strikeouts: Roger _ _ _

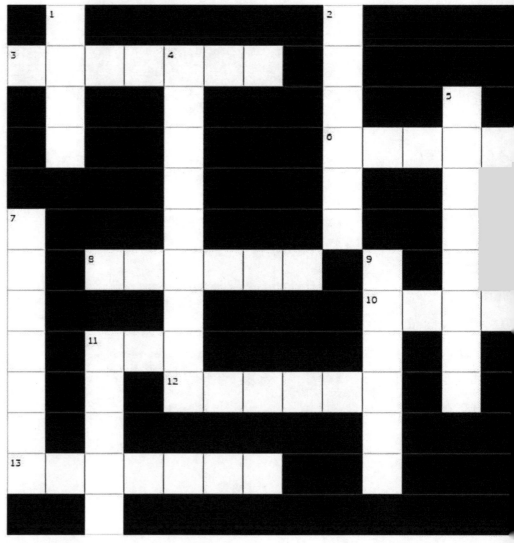

DOWN

1 Japanese pitcher known for his "Tornado" pitch and high strikeout numbers

2 Record-holder for most strikeouts in a single game

4 The pitcher who holds the record for the most strikeouts in a postseason

5 The term for a batter striking out three times in a game

7 The term for a batter striking out five times in a game: _ _ _ Rings

9 Number of strikeouts recorded by Kerry Wood in his famous 1998 game

11 The number of strikeouts needed by a pitcher to record an immaculate inning: _ _ _ strikeouts

13- Double Plays

ACROSS

2 MLB player with the most career double plays turned as a catcher: Ray ___

5 The MLB player who holds the record for the most career double plays turned as a second baseman: Ryne ___

7 The MLB team with the fewest double plays turned in a single season

9 The number of outs recorded in a typical double play

11 MLB player with the most career double plays turned as a center fielder: Tris ___

12 The fielding position often associated with starting a double play: ___ base

13 The MLB player who holds the record for the most career double plays turned as a shortstop: ___ Smith

14 Team with the most double plays grounded into in 1990 season

15 The MLB player who holds the record for the most career double plays turned as a third baseman: ___ Robinson

DOWN

1 Number of players involved in a typical 6-4-3 double play

3 Team with the highest double play percentage in 2023

4 The MLB player who holds the record for the most career double plays turned as a first baseman overall: Mickey ___

6 The MLB team with the fewest double plays turned in a single season, recording only 94 double plays in 2021

7 The number of outs required for a triple play

8 The MLB team with the most double plays turned in a single season

10 The MLB player who holds the record for the most career double plays turned as a pitcher: Greg ___

14- Grand Slam

ACROSS

2 The MLB player who has hit the most grand slams in his career

5 The player who has the most grand slams in a single MLB season: Don _ _ _

7 What MLB team has the most grand slams in a season?

9 Who hit the grand slam in the 2021 World Series?

10 The number of grand slams hit by Don Mattingly in his MLB career

11 The number of grand slams hit by Fernando Tatis Sr. in a single inning

12 The number of runs scored on a grand slam

13 The player who holds the record for the most grand slams in a single MLB season: Travis _ _ _

DOWN

1 The MLB team with the longest streak of consecutive games with a grand slam

3 The term for a home run hit with the bases loaded

4 The MLB player who hit the most grand slams in 2023: _ _ _ Lewis

6 The term for a grand slam hit by the first batter of the game: _ _ _ Grand Slam

8 The number of career grand slams hit by Babe Ruth

15- MVP Winners

ACROSS

1 The MLB player who won the National League MVP award in 2016: Kris _ _ _

4 The MLB player who won the most MVP awards in their career: _ _ _ Bonds

6 The MLB player who won the American League MVP award in 2019: Mike _ _ _

8 The MLB player who won the National League MVP award in 2017: Giancarlo _ _ _

10 The MLB player who won the National League MVP award in 2021: Bryce _ _ _

11 The number of times Babe Ruth won the American League MVP award.

12 The award given to the most valuable player in the American League: _ _ _ Award

13 The MLB player who won the American League MVP award in 2021: Shohei _ _ _

DOWN

1 The MLB player who won the National League MVP award in 2019: Cody _ _ _

2 The MLB player who won the National League MVP award in 2018: Christian _ _ _

3 The MLB player who won the first MVP award in 1911: _ _ _ Cobb

4 The MLB player who won the American League MVP award in 2018: Mookie _ _ _

5 The MLB player who won the American League MVP award in 2020: José _ _ _

7 The MLB player who won the National League MVP award in 2020: Freddie _ _ _

9 The MLB player who won the American League MVP award in 2017: José _ _ _

16- Cy Young Winners

ACROSS

1 The MLB pitcher who won the American League Cy Young Award in 2020: Shane _ _ _

4 The award given to the best pitcher in the American League: _ _ _ Young Award

5 The MLB pitcher with the most Cy Young Awards in their career: _ _ _ Johnson

8 The number of times Roger Clemens won the Cy Young Award

10 The MLB pitcher who won the American League Cy Young Award in 2016: Rick _ _ _

12 The MLB pitcher who won the first Cy Young Award in 1956: Don _ _ _

13 The MLB pitcher who won the National League Cy Young Award in 2020: _ _ _ deGrom

14 The MLB pitcher who won the National League Cy Young Award in 2017: Max _ _ _

15 The MLB pitcher who won the American League Cy Young Award in 2018: Blake _ _ _

DOWN

1 The MLB pitcher who won the National League Cy Young Award in 2020: Trevor _ _ _

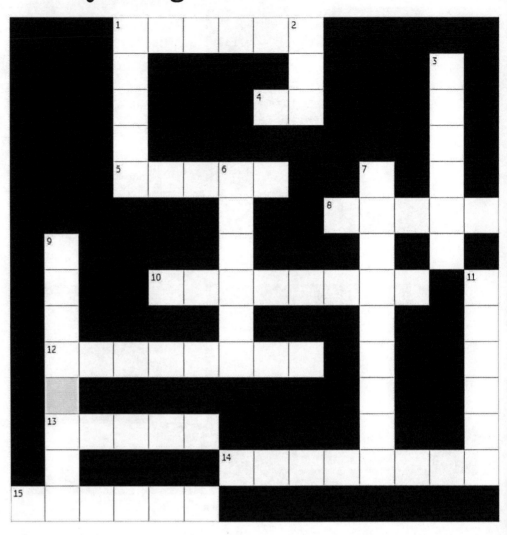

2 The MLB pitcher who won the American League Cy Young Award in 2021: Robbie _ _

3 The MLB pitcher who won the National League Cy Young Award in 2021: Corbin _ _ _

6 The MLB pitcher who won the National League Cy Young Award in 2019: Jacob _ _ _

7 The MLB pitcher who won the American League Cy Young Award in 2019: Justin _ _ _

9 The MLB pitcher who won the National League Cy Young Award in 2019: _ _ _ Ryu

11 The MLB pitcher who won the American League Cy Young Award in 2017: Corey _ _ _

17- Rookie Stars

ACROSS

1 The MLB player who won the National League Rookie of the Year award in 2018: Ronald ___ Jr.

5 The MLB player who won the American League Rookie of the Year award in 2021: ___ García

8 The MLB player who won the American League Rookie of the Year award in 2019: Yordan ___

9 The award given to the best rookie player in the American League: ___ of the Year

11 The number of players who win the Rookie of the Year award each year in each league

13 The MLB player who won the National League Rookie of the Year award in 2020: Devin ___

16 The MLB player who won the American League Rookie of the Year award in 2017: Aaron ___

17 The MLB player who won the American League Rookie of the Year award in 2014: José ___

DOWN

2 The MLB player who won the American League Rookie of the Year award in 2015: Carlos ___

3 The MLB player who won the American League Rookie of the Year award in 2016: Michael ___

4 The MLB player who won the National League Rookie of the Year award in 2015: Kris ___

6 The MLB player who won the National League Rookie of the Year award in 2017: Cody ___

7 The MLB player who won the American League Rookie of the Year award in 2020: Kyle ___

10 The MLB player who won the American League Rookie of the Year award in 2018: Shohei ___

12 The MLB player who won the National League Rookie of the Year award in 2019: Pete ___

14 The MLB player who won the National League Rookie of the Year award in 2016: Corey ___

15 The MLB player who won the National League Rookie of the Year award in 2021: Jonathan ___

18- Perfect Game

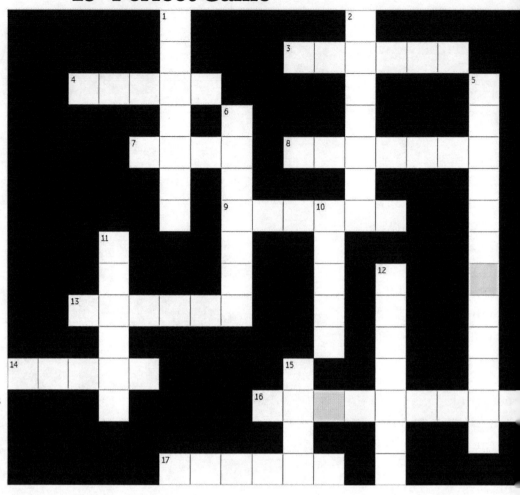

ACROSS

3 The number of strikeouts recorded in Dennis Martínez's perfect game in 1991

4 The MLB pitcher who threw the first perfect game in the modern era in 1904: Cy _ _ _

7 The number of perfect games thrown in the 19th century.

8 The MLB pitcher who threw a perfect game while playing for the Chicago White Sox in 2009: Mark _ _ _

9 The MLB team that has pitched the most perfect games in history

13 The MLB team that has been the opponent in the most perfect games in history

14 The number of pitchers involved in a combined perfect game thrown by the Los Angeles Dodgers in 2020

16 The term for a game in which no opposing player reaches base, but not all outs are strikeouts: _ _ _ Game

17 The MLB pitcher who threw the most recent perfect game in 2012: Philip _ _ _

DOWN

1 The MLB team that has been the opponent in the most perfect games in history

2 The term for a game in which no opposing player reaches base: _ _ _ Game

5 The number of total perfect games in MLB history as of 2022

6 The MLB team that has been the opponent in the most perfect games in history

10 The MLB pitcher with the most perfect games in their career: _ _ _ Ryan

11 The MLB pitcher who threw a perfect game while playing for the Oakland Athletics in 2010: Dallas _ _ _

12 The MLB pitcher who threw a perfect game while playing for the Philadelphia Phillies in 1964: Jim _ _ _

15 The MLB pitcher who threw a perfect game while playing for the New York Yankees in 1999: David _ _ _

19- Base Hits

ACROSS

4 The term for a hit in which the batter reaches third base safely.

5 The MLB player with the most career base hits: Pete _ _ _

8 The term for a hit in which the batter reaches second base safely.

11 The MLB team with the most base hits in a single game: _ _ _ Red Sox

13 The MLB player who holds the record for the most hits in a single season: Ichiro _ _ _

15 The MLB team with the fewest base hits in a single game: _ _ _ Orioles

16 The MLB player who holds the record for the most hits by a rookie in a single season: _ _ _ Jeter

DOWN

1 The term for a hit in which the batter hits the ball and safely reaches first base on an error by the fielder: _ _ _ Single

2 The number of hits recorded by Ty Cobb in his MLB career

3 The term for a hit in which the batter reaches first base safely.

6 The MLB player with the most hits in the 1980s: Robin _ _ _

7 The term for a hit in which the batter reaches first base safely after hitting a ground ball through the infield: _ _ _ Single

9 The term for a hit in which the batter reaches first base safely after hitting the ball sharply and it bounces over an infielder: _ _ _ Single

10 The term for a hit in which the batter reaches first base safely after hitting the ball into the outfield: Outfield _ _ _

12 The MLB player with the most hits in a single season before Ichiro Suzuki broke the record: George _ _ _

14 The term for a hit in which the batter reaches first base safely after hitting the ball into the outfield and the fielder is unable to make a play: _ _ _ Single

20- Triple Play

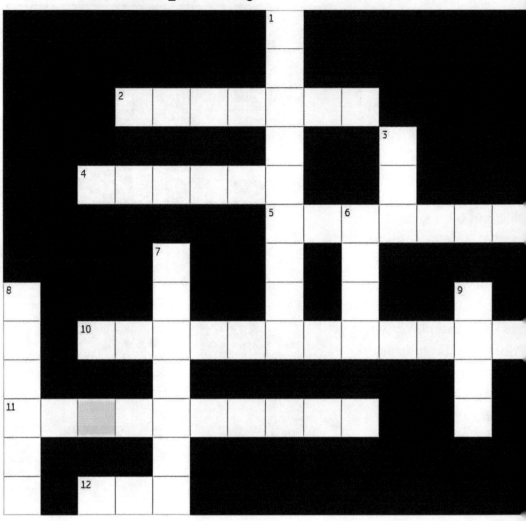

ACROSS

2 The number of unassisted triple plays in MLB history as of 2022

4 The term for a defensive play resulting in three outs: _ _ _ Play

5 The term for a triple play initiated by the shortstop, who catches a line drive, steps on second base, and tags a runner: _ _ _ Triple Play

10 The MLB team that turned the most triple plays in a single season: _ _ _ Phillies

11 The MLB team that turned the most triple plays in history as of 2022

12 The number of unassisted triple plays turned by Ron Hansen, tying the MLB record

DOWN

1 The MLB team that turned the most unassisted triple plays in history: _ _ _ Indians

3 The MLB player who turned the most triple plays as a shortstop: _ _ _ Tinker

6 The MLB player who holds the record for the most career unassisted triple plays: _ _ _ Fisher

7 The MLB team that turned the most triple plays in a single game, achieving three triple plays on September 21, 1920: _ _ _ White Sox

8 The MLB player who turned the most unassisted triple plays in history: _ _ _ Smith

9 The number of triple plays turned by the Oakland Athletics in the 2010s, the most by any team in a single decade

21- Walk-Off Wins

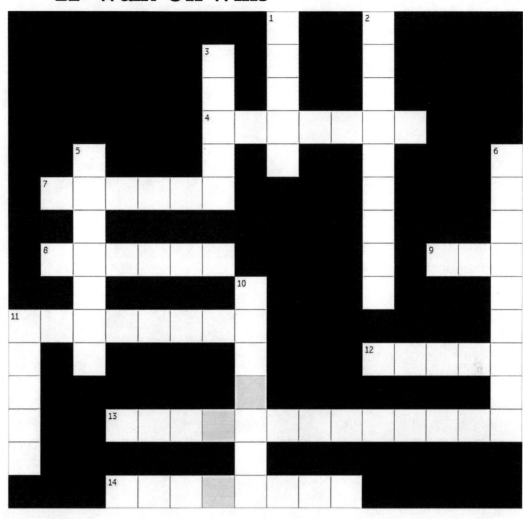

ACROSS

4 MLB team with the fewest walk-off wins in a single season: Baltimore _ _ _

7 MLB player who hit the most walk-off home runs in a single season, hitting six in 1961: Mickey _ _ _

8 Number of walk-off wins by the Boston Red Sox in the 2013 season, tying the MLB record

9 MLB player who hit the most walk-off grand slams in a single season: _ _ _ Griffey Jr.

11 MLB player who hit a walk-off home run to win Game 7 of the 1997 World Series for the Florida Marlins: Edgar _ _ _

12 The term for a walk-off win achieved with a game-ending home run: _ _ _ Walk-Off

13 MLB team with the most walk-off wins in history as of 2022: _ _ _ Giants

14 MLB team with the most walk-off wins in a single season: _ _ _ Yankees

DOWN

1 MLB player who hit a walk-off home run in Game 7 of the 2016 World Series: Rajai _ _ _

2 MLB player who hit a walk-off home run to win Game 7 of the 1960 World Series for the Pittsburgh Pirates: Bill _ _ _

3 The player who hit the most walk-off home runs in MLB history: Jim _ _ _

5 MLB team with the most walk-off wins in a single postseason: _ _ _ Athletics

6 MLB player who hit the most walk-off home runs in the 2010s: _ _ _ Stanton

10 The term for a walk-off sacrifice fly: _ _ _ Walk-Off

11 MLB player who hit a walk-off grand slam in Game 5 of the 2017 NLDS: Anthony _ _ _

22- No-Hitters

ACROSS

2 Pitcher who threw a no-hitter while pitching for the San Francisco Giants in 2015: Chris _ _ _

5 Team with the most combined no-hitters in a single postseason (2021): _ _ _ Padres

8 Pitcher with the most strikeouts in a single no-hitter game: _ _ _ Johnson

9 Game in which a pitcher allows no hits: _ _ _ Game

12 Number of no-hitters thrown by Sandy Koufax

15 Pitcher with the most recent no-hitter in 2022: _ _ _ Scherzer

16 Pitcher with the most career no-hitters in the National League: Sandy _ _ _

17 Team with the most combined no-hitters in history: _ _ _ Astros

DOWN

1 Pitcher with the most recent no-hitter in the American League in 2022: _ _ _ Rodón

2 Pitcher who threw a no-hitter while pitching for the Philadelphia Phillies in 2010: Roy _ _ _

3 Pitcher with the most recent no-hitter in 2022: _ _ _ Means

4 Pitcher with the most recent perfect game in 2022: _ _ _ Kershaw

6 Pitcher who threw the first combined no-hitter in MLB history in 1917: _ _ _ Alexander

7 Pitcher who threw the first perfect game in MLB history in 1880: John _ _ _

10 Team with the most no-hitters in a single season in the modern era (since 1900)

11 Pitcher with the most career no-hitters: _ _ _ Ryan

13 Pitcher with the most recent perfect game in the National League in 2012: Matt _ _ _

14 Team with the most consecutive seasons without being no-hit

23- ERA Leaders

ACROSS

2 Pitcher with the lowest single-season ERA in the 19th century (since 1893): ___ Young

5 Pitcher with the lowest single-season ERA in MLB history (1914): ___ Johnson

7 Pitcher with the lowest single-season ERA in the American League (since 1972): Ron ___

9 Pitcher with the lowest career ERA in MLB history (dead-ball era): ___ Plank

13 Pitcher with the lowest career ERA among pitchers with at least 3,000 innings pitched: ___ Alexander

15 Pitcher with the lowest career ERA among left-handed pitchers (modern era): Sandy ___

16 Pitcher with the lowest single-season ERA in the National League (since 1969): Dwight ___

DOWN

1 Pitcher with the lowest single-season ERA in the 20th century (1905): Christy ___

2 Pitcher with the lowest career ERA among Hall of Famers: ___ Mathewson

3 Pitcher with the lowest single-season ERA in the 21st century (2000): Pedro ___

4 Pitcher with the lowest career ERA among active relievers (as of 2022): ___ Chapman

6 Pitcher with the lowest single-season ERA in the American League (since 1920): Lefty ___

7 Pitcher with the lowest single-season ERA in the National League (since 1920): Bob ___

8 Pitcher with the lowest career ERA in MLB history (19th century): ___ Galvin

10 Pitcher with the lowest career ERA among active players (as of 2022): Jacob ___

11 Pitcher with the lowest single-season ERA in the National League (since 1972): Greg ___

12 Pitcher with the lowest single-season ERA in the American League (since 1969): ___ Martinez

14 Pitcher with the lowest career ERA in MLB history (modern era): ___ Marichal

24- RBI Leaders

ACROSS

2 Player with the most career RBIs among active switch-hitters (as of 2022): Carlos _ _ _

6 Player with the most career RBIs among active players (as of 2022): Albert _ _ _

7 Player with the most career RBIs among Hall of Famers: Stan _ _ _

8 Player with the most career RBIs in MLB history: _ _ _ Ruth

9 Player with the most RBIs in a single season in the live-ball era (since 1920): Lou _ _ _

11 Player with the most career RBIs in the live-ball era (since 1920): Alex _ _ _

12 Player with the most RBIs in a single season in the National League (since 1977): Andre _ _ _

14 Player with the most RBIs in a single season in the 20th century (1930): Chuck _ _ _

15 Player with the most RBIs in a single season in MLB history (1911): _ _ _ Wagner

DOWN

1 Player with the most career RBIs in the 19th century: _ _ _ Anson

3 Player with the most RBIs in a single season in the American League (since 1969): Manny _ _ _

4 Player with the most RBIs in a single season in the 21st century (2000): Sammy _ _ _

5 Player with the most career RBIs among left-handed hitters (modern era): Carl _ _ _

8 Player with the most career RBIs among catchers: Yogi _ _ _

10 Player with the most RBIs in a single season in the National League (since 1920): Hank _ _ _

13 Player with the most RBIs in a single season in the American League (since 1920): Hack _ _ _

25- Batting Average

ACROSS

1 Player with the highest career batting average among catchers: Mickey _ _ _

4 Player with the highest single-season batting average in the live-ball era (since 1920): George _ _ _

8 Player with the highest single-season batting average in the 21st century (2000): Ichiro _ _ _

10 Player with the highest career batting average among active players (as of 2022): Miguel _ _ _

11 Player with the highest single-season batting average in the National League (since 1969): Tony _ _ _

13 Player with the highest single-season batting average in the American League (since 1969): _ _ _ Carew

14 Player with the highest career batting average among active switch-hitters (as of 2022): _ _ _ Albies

15 Player with the highest career batting average among left-handed hitters (modern era): _ _ _ Williams

DOWN

2 Player with the highest single-season batting average in MLB history (since 1900): _ _ _ Hornsby

3 Player with the highest career batting average in the 19th century: _ _ _ Keeler

5 Player with the highest single-season batting average in the National League (since 1900): Hugh _ _ _

6 Player with the highest career batting average among Hall of Famers: Shoeless Joe _ _ _

7 Player with the highest career batting average in MLB history (minimum 3,000 plate appearances): Ty _ _ _

9 Player with the highest single-season batting average in the American League (since 1900): Nap _ _ _

12 Player with the highest single-season batting average in the 19th century (since 1876): _ _ _ O'Rourke

26- Golden Glove

ACROSS

4 MLB team with the most Gold Glove Awards in a single season (2002): ___ Mariners

5 Player with the most Gold Glove Awards at second base: Ryne ___

9 Player with the most Gold Glove Awards at second base: Roberto ___

12 Player with the most Gold Glove Awards in a single season (1979): ___ Griffey Jr.

13 Player with the most Gold Glove Awards at shortstop: ___ Smith

14 Player with the most Gold Glove Awards at shortstop: ___ Ripken Jr.

15 Player with the most Gold Glove Awards at outfield: ___ Jones

DOWN

1 Player with the most Gold Glove Awards at outfield: ___ Mays

2 Player with the most Gold Glove Awards at outfield: Al ___

3 Player with the most Gold Glove Awards at second base: Bill ___

6 Player with the most Gold Glove Awards at outfield: Ken ___ Jr.

7 MLB team with the most Gold Glove Awards in the 1980s: ___ Athletics

8 Player with the most Gold Glove Awards at third base: ___ Robinson

10 Player with the most Gold Glove Awards at catcher: Johnny ___

11 Player with the most Gold Glove Awards at third base: Scott ___

27- Pinch Hitters

ACROSS

1 Player with the most pinch-hit at-bats in a single season (1985): Larry _ _ _

3 Player with the most pinch-hit at-bats in a single season (2008): _ _ _ Valentin

5 Player with the most pinch-hit at-bats in a single season (1969): _ _ _ Cash

8 Player with the most career pinch-hit home runs as a switch hitter

10 Player with the most career pinch-hit RBIs in MLB history: _ _ _ Biggio

11 Player with the most career pinch-hit home runs in MLB history: _ _ _ Morales

13 Player with the most pinch-hit RBIs in a single season (1976): _ _ _ Johnson

DOWN

2 Player with the most pinch-hit home runs in a single season (1993): Lenny _ _ _

4 Player with the most career pinch-hit doubles in MLB history: Matt _ _ _

6 Player with the most pinch-hit at-bats in a single season (1975): Del _ _ _

7 Player with the most career pinch-hit triples in MLB history: Dave _ _ _

9 Player with the most career pinch-hit triples in a single season (1907): Germany _ _ _

12 Player with the most pinch-hit at-bats in a single season (2011): _ _ _ Castro

28- Bullpen Heroes

ACROSS

3 Pitcher with the most saves in a single postseason series (2019): _ _ _ Osuna

7 Pitcher with the most saves in a single postseason: _ _ _ Chapman

8 Pitcher with the most saves in a single month in MLB history: Eric _ _ _

11 Pitcher with the most saves in a single season in MLB history (2008): Francisco _ _ _

13 Pitcher with the most saves in a single All-Star Game: _ _ _ Fingers

15 Pitcher with the most saves in a single World Series (2002): Troy _ _ _

DOWN

1 Pitcher with the most saves in a single postseason series: _ _ _ Lidge

2 Pitcher with the most career strikeouts as a reliever in MLB history: _ _ _ Smith

4 Pitcher with the most saves in a single season in the American League (1990): Bobby _ _ _

5 Pitcher with the most career saves in MLB history: _ _ _ Rivera

6 Pitcher with the most saves in a single World Series: _ _ _ Eckersley

9 Pitcher with the most saves in a single World Baseball Classic: _ _ _ Holland

10 Pitcher with the most career wins as a reliever in MLB history: John _ _ _

12 Pitcher with the most saves in a single World Series game (2015): _ _ _ Davis

14 Pitcher with the most saves in a single season by a rookie (2019): _ _ _ Hendriks

29- Leadoff Hitters

ACROSS

2 Player with the most leadoff RBIs in a single season (2006): Alfonso _ _ _

5 Player with the most leadoff stolen bases in a single season (1982): Willie _ _ _

6 Player with the most leadoff doubles in a single season (1978): Charlie _ _ _

8 Player with the most leadoff doubles in a single season (2019): _ _ _ Merrifield

9 Player with the most leadoff home runs in a single season (1996): Brady _ _ _

10 Player with the most leadoff triples in a single season (1912): Clyde _ _ _

13 Player with the most consecutive games reaching base as the leadoff hitter (2017)": DJ _ _ _

15 Player with the most leadoff hits in a single season (2016): _ _ _ Fowler

16 Player with the most leadoff runs scored in a single season (1954): _ _ _ Ashburn

17 Player with the most leadoff stolen bases in a single season (1977): Omar _ _ _

DOWN

1 Player with the most leadoff RBIs in a single season (1987): _ _ _ Vince

3 Player with the most seasons leading off with at least 200 hits (Most Seasons)

4 Player with the most leadoff runs scored in a single season (1932): Chuck _ _ _

7 Player with the most leadoff doubles in a single season (1996): Jay _ _ _

11 Player with the most leadoff runs scored in a single season (2016): _ _ _ Fowler

12 Player with the most leadoff RBIs in a single season (1976): _ _ _ Lopes

14 Player with the most leadoff triples in a single season (1994): _ _ _ Jaha

30- Double Headers

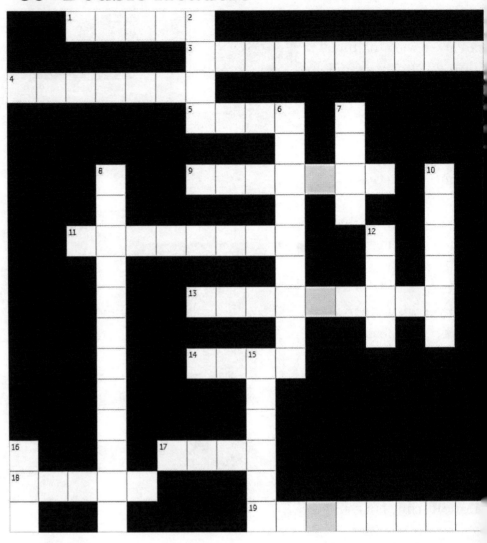

ACROSS

1 The term for two games played on the same day but not consecutively: _ _ _ Doubleheader

3 The last team to play a traditional scheduled doubleheader in MLB before rule changes

4 The player who hit four home runs in a doubleheader on May 24, 1936: Tony _ _ _

5 The number of innings typically played in each game of a doubleheader

9 The official term for a doubleheader played as a result of a postponed game

11 The team hosting a doubleheader that plays the first game: _ _ _ Team

13 The type of doubleheader where the second game is scheduled only if the first game is not a tie

14 The month with the most historically scheduled doubleheaders in MLB

17 The team hosting a doubleheader that plays the second game: _ _ _ Team

18 The month with the fewest historically scheduled doubleheaders in MLB

19 The last team to schedule a traditional doubleheader before MLB's rule changes

DOWN

2 The term for a scheduled doubleheader in which fans buy one ticket for both games: _ _ _ Header

6 The term for a doubleheader played due to an unforeseen circumstance, like a tie game: _ _ _ Header

7 The number of days in advance a traditional doubleheader could be scheduled in MLB before rule changes

8 The MLB team that played the most doubleheaders in a single season (1943)

10 The term for two baseball games played consecutively on the same day at the same venue: _ _ _ Header

12 The most common reason for scheduling doubleheaders

15 The team often scheduled for doubleheaders to make up postponed games

16 The term for a doubleheader where one team plays two games in one day: _ _ _ Header

31- Spring Training

ACROSS

3 Pitchers and catchers report here for spring training

8 Term for the set of practices and exhibition games that occur before the regular season

10 Location of the "Grapefruit League"

12 Number of weeks typically spent in spring training

13 Term for the period before the regular season starts

14 Exhibition games between Major League teams and their minor league affiliates during spring training

16 Grapefruit League team based in Arizona

17 Team's practice games during the spring

DOWN

1 Area where spring training games are played

2 Stadium where the Grapefruit League plays

3 Spring training location in Florida

4 Practice games played by MLB teams during spring training

5 Primary objective of spring training games: Player _ _ _

6 Players who are not on the Major League roster during spring training: Minor _ _ _

7 What players use to practice hitting during spring training: Batting

_ _ _

9 Length of a typical spring training game: _ _ _ _ innings

11 Annual spring training championship game in Arizona

15 Spring training location in Arizona

32- Playoffs Bound

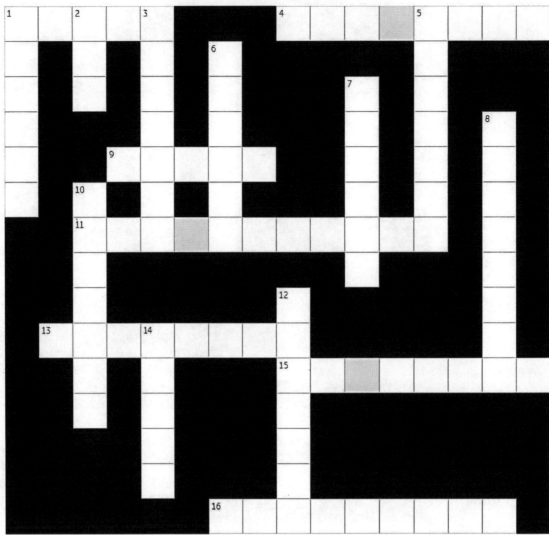

ACROSS

1 Manager with the most postseason series wins: Bruce _ _ _

4 City with the most World Series championships

9 Player with the most career postseason hits: Derek _ _ _

11 City with the most MLB playoff teams in 2022

13 Pitcher with the most career postseason wins: Andy _ _ _

15 Manager with the most postseason appearances: Tony _ _ _

16 Player with the most career postseason stolen bases: Rickey _ _ _

DOWN

1 Team with the most consecutive playoff appearances (1995-2007): Atlanta _ _ _

2 Manager with the most postseason ejections: Bobby _ _ _

3 Team with the most World Series appearances

5 Team with the most postseason victories in a single season (1998)

6 Player with the most career postseason saves: Mariano _ _ _

7 Player with the most career postseason home runs: Albert _ _ _

8 Team with the longest playoff drought (as of 2022): Seattle _ _ _

10 Pitcher with the most career postseason strikeouts: Roger _ _ _

12 Player with the most postseason RBIs in a single season (2004): Carlos _ _ _

14 Manager with the most World Series titles: Joe _ _

33- Wildcard Race

ACROSS

1 Player who hit a dramatic walk-off single in the 2014 American League Wild Card Game for the Kansas City Royals: Salvador _ _ _

5 Player who hit a memorable walk-off grand slam in the 2019 National League Wild Card Game: Juan _ _ _

8 Team that clinched the second Wild Card spot in the National League in 2021, earning a playoff berth for the first time in over a decade: Cincinnati _ _ _

9 Team that won the first-ever American League Wild Card Game in 2012: Baltimore _ _ _

12 Manager who led the Tampa Bay Rays to the Wild Card Game in 2019 despite having one of the lowest payrolls in MLB: Kevin _ _ _

13 City that hosted the first-ever American League Wild Card Game in 2012

16 Manager who led the Oakland Athletics to multiple Wild Card berths in the 2010s: Bob _ _ _

17 Team that won the first-ever National League Wild Card Game in 2012: St. Louis _ _ _

DOWN

2 Team that secured the final Wild Card spot in the American League in 2022

3 Player who hit the game-winning home run to clinch a Wild Card berth for the Chicago Cubs in 2021: Patrick _ _ _

4 Player who hit a walk-off single in the 2015 National League Wild Card Game for the Chicago Cubs: Dexter _ _ _

6 Player who set the record for the most strikeouts in a single Wild Card game in 2018: Luis _ _ _

7 Player who hit a walk-off home run to clinch the second Wild Card spot for the San Francisco Giants in 2016: Conor _ _ _

10 City that hosted the first-ever National League Wild Card Game in 2012

11 Number of teams that compete in the Wild Card Game

14 Number of Wild Card teams in each league

15 Team that famously won the Wild Card game with a walk-off home run by Edwin Encarnacion in 2016: Blue _ _ _

34- Playoff MVP

ACROSS

1 Outfielder who won the World Series MVP award with the San Francisco Giants in 2014: Madison ___

6 Pitcher who won the World Series MVP award with the San Francisco Giants in 2012: Pablo ___

8 Shortstop who won the World Series MVP award with the Houston Astros in 2017: George ___

9 Pitcher who won the World Series MVP award with the Toronto Blue Jays in 1992: Pat ___

11 Pitcher who won the World Series MVP award with the Philadelphia Phillies in 2008: Cole ___

13 Catcher who won the World Series MVP award with the Boston Red Sox in 2013: David ___

14 Pitcher who won the World Series MVP award with the Arizona Diamondbacks in 2001: Randy ___

15 Pitcher who won the World Series MVP award with the Kansas City Royals in 2015: Salvador ___

16 Player who won the World Series MVP award with the Boston Red Sox in 2018: Steve ___

DOWN

2 Outfielder who won the World Series MVP award with the New York Yankees in 2009: Hideki ___

3 Player who won the World Series MVP award with the St. Louis Cardinals in 2011: David ___

4 Pitcher who won the World Series MVP award with the Chicago Cubs in 2016: Ben ___

5 Third baseman who won the World Series MVP award with the Kansas City Royals in 1985: Bret ___

7 Player who won the World Series MVP award with the Philadelphia Phillies in 2009 Cole ___

10 Outfielder who won the World Series MVP award with the San Francisco Giants in 2010: Edgar ___

12 Shortstop who won the World Series MVP award with the Cincinnati Reds in 1990: Frank ___

35- Extra Innings

ACROSS

5 The team with the most extra-inning games won in a single MLB season: ___ White Sox

7 The city that hosted the longest MLB game by innings

11 The player who hit the game-winning home run in the longest MLB game by innings: Bobby ___

13 The pitcher with the most innings pitched in a single MLB extra-inning game: Leon ___

14 Player who holds the record for the most career extra-inning home runs: Albert ___

15 The team with the most extra-inning wins in a single MLB season: New York ___

DOWN

1 The longest MLB game by time with extra innings played: ___ Hours

2 The team that played in the longest MLB game by innings: ___ Red Wings

3 The term for a game tied after nine innings and forced into extra innings

4 The term for a game that extends beyond the regulation nine innings

6 Term for a game-ending hit in extra innings

8 The term for a game tied after nine innings and forced into extra innings

9 The pitcher with the most career extra-inning strikeouts: Roger ___

10 The player who hit the game-winning hit in the longest MLB game by time: Ted ___

12 The player with the most career extra-inning hits: Pete ___

36- Postseason Glory

ACROSS

2 Team with the most World Series titles: New York _ _ _

4 Player with the most career postseason home runs: _ _ _ Rodriguez

7 The team that won the inaugural World Series in 1903: Boston _ _ _

9 Manager who led the New York Mets to a World Series championship in 1969: Gil _ _

10 Outfielder who hit three home runs in Game 1 of the 1977 World Series: Reggie _ _ _

12 Player with the most career postseason saves: Mariano _ _ _

13 The team with the most consecutive postseason appearances (1995-2005): Atlanta _ _ _

15 Pitcher with the most strikeouts in a single postseason game: Bob _ _ _

DOWN

1 City with the most World Series championships

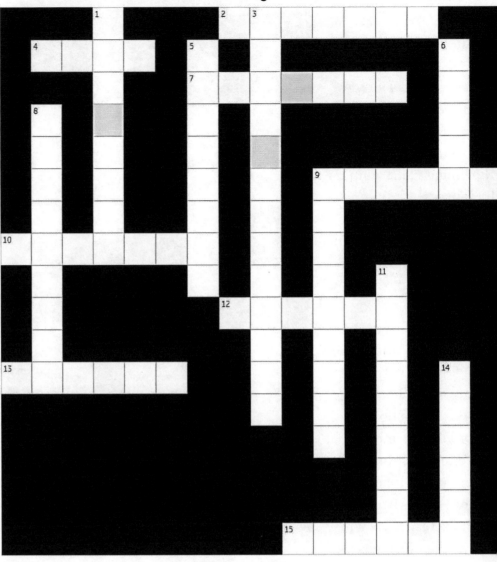

3 Pitcher with the most career postseason wins

5 Manager who led the Boston Red Sox to their first World Series championship in 86 years in 2004: Terry _ _ _

6 Manager with the most World Series titles: Joe _ _ _

8 Pitcher who won both the Cy Young Award and the World Series MVP in 2014: Madison _ _ _

9 Player with the most career postseason stolen bases: Rickey _ _ _

11 Team with the most postseason appearances in MLB history

14 Pitcher who threw a perfect game in the 1956 World Series: Don _ _ _

37- Manager Names

ACROSS

4 Former manager of the Los Angeles Dodgers who won the NL Manager of the Year award multiple times: Tommy _ _ _

6 Manager of the Houston Astros who led the team to its first World Series championship in 2017: A.J. _ _ _

7 Hall of Fame manager who led the Cincinnati Reds to two World Series titles in the 1970s: _ _ _ Anderson

9 Manager of the Chicago White Sox who led the team to a World Series championship in 2005: Ozzie _ _ _

11 Manager of the New York Mets who guided the team to a World Series championship in 1986: Davey _ _ _

13 Manager of the Chicago Cubs who ended the team's 108-year championship drought in 2016: Joe _ _ _

14 Current manager of the Los Angeles Dodgers, known for his analytical approach to the game

16 Manager of the New York Yankees who became the youngest manager to win a World Series: Aaron _ _ _

17 Manager of the Toronto Blue Jays who led the team to back-to-back World Series championships in 1992 and 1993: Cito _ _ _

18 Hall of Fame manager of the New York Yankees who won 10 World Series titles: Casey _ _ _

DOWN

1 Former manager of the St. Louis Cardinals, known for his emphasis on fundamentals and player development: Tony _ _ _

2 Manager of the San Francisco Giants who led the team to multiple World Series championships in the 2010s: Bruce _ _ _

3 Former manager of the Philadelphia Phillies who led the team to a World Series championship in 2008: Charlie _ _ _

5 Former manager of the Los Angeles Angels who led the team to its first and only World Series championship in 2002: Mike _ _ _

8 Manager of the Kansas City Royals who won the World Series with the team in 2015

10 Manager of the Chicago Cubs who won the World Series with the team in 1907 and 1908: Frank _ _ _

12 Hall of Fame manager who led the Baltimore Orioles to multiple World Series appearances in the 1960s and 1970s: Earl _ _ _

15 Manager of the Oakland Athletics depicted in the film "Moneyball": Billy _ _ _

38- Rookie of the Year

ACROSS

1 First baseman who won the NL Rookie of the Year award in 2020, helping lead his team to a World Series championship: Devin _ _ _

3 Infielder who won the AL Rookie of the Year award in 2016, hitting .315 with 20 home runs and 72 RBIs: Gary _ _ _

5 Shortstop who won the NL Rookie of the Year award in 2016, hitting .273 with 21 home runs and 62 RBIs: Corey _ _ _

6 Outfielder who won the AL Rookie of the Year award in 2018, setting the rookie record for most home runs by a teenager: Juan _ _ _

7 Hall of Famer who won the AL Rookie of the Year award in 1956 and went on to have a legendary career with the New York Yankees: Mickey _ _ _

10 MLB Rookie of the Year in 2019, who set the single-season rookie home run record with 53: Pete _ _ _

11 Outfielder who won the AL Rookie of the Year award in 2017 and was a key part of the Houston Astros' World Series-winning team that year: Aaron _ _ _

12 Infielder who won the AL Rookie of the Year award in 2014, leading the league in hits, doubles, and runs scored: José _ _ _

DOWN

2 Pitcher who won the AL Rookie of the Year award in 2013, leading the league in strikeouts and innings pitched: Wil _ _ _

4 Infielder who won the AL Rookie of the Year award in 2015 becoming the first unanimous winner in the award's history: Carlos _ _ _

8 Pitcher who won the NL Rookie of the Year award in 2018 and played a crucial role in the Atlanta Braves' playoff run that year: Ronald _ _ _

9 Outfielder who won the NL Rookie of the Year award in 202 helping his team make a deep postseason run: Jonathan _ _ _

39- Cy Young Winners

ACROSS

1 Pitcher who won the NL Cy Young Award in 2015 with the Chicago Cubs

3 Pitcher who won the AL Cy Young Award in 2009 with the New York Yankees: Zack _ _ _

5 Hall of Famer who won the NL Cy Young Award three times with the Los Angeles Dodgers in the 1960s: Sandy _ _ _

6 Pitcher who won the AL Cy Young Award in 2014 with the Tampa Bay Rays: David _ _ _

8 The first pitcher to win the AL Cy Young Award in back-to-back seasons (2016 and 2017): Corey _ _ _

11 Pitcher who won the AL Cy Young Award in 2020 with the Cleveland Indians: Shane _ _ _

12 Pitcher who won the NL Cy Young Award in 2016 with the Washington Nationals: Max _ _ _

13 Pitcher who won the AL Cy Young Award in 2018 and 2019 with the Houston Astros: Justin _ _ _

DOWN

2 The only reliever to win the AL Cy Young Award, doing so with the Oakland Athletics in 1992: Dennis _ _ _

4 Pitcher who won the AL Cy Young Award in 2021 with the Toronto Blue Jays: Robbie _ _ _

5 Pitcher who won the NL Cy Young Award in 2014 with the Los Angeles Dodgers: Clayton _ _ _

7 Pitcher who won the NL Cy Young Award in 2021 with the Milwaukee Brewers: Corbin _ _ _

8 Pitcher who won the AL Cy Young Award in 2015 with the Houston Astros: Dallas _ _ _

9 Pitcher who won the NL Cy Young Award in 2013 with the New York Mets: R.A. _ _ _

10 Pitcher who won the NL Cy Young Award in 2019 with the New York Mets: Jacob _ _ _

40- Defensive Gems

ACROSS

1 Third baseman who made a diving catch in foul territory during the 1991 World Series

3 Infielder known for his diving stop and throw in the 2001 World Series: Scott _ _ _

4 Outfielder who made an incredible catch while flipping over the outfield wall in the 1982 ALCS: Rick _ _ _

6 First baseman who made a famous diving catch in the 1980 World Series: Keith _ _ _

8 Outfielder who made a leaping catch over the wall to rob a home run in the 1982 ALCS: George _ _ _

10 Shortstop known for his acrobatic catches, such as the "Jeterian" play: Derek _ _ _

13 Outfielder famous for "The Catch" in the 1954 World Series: Willie _ _ _

14 Outfielder who made a diving catch to save a perfect game in 2010: Austin _ _ _

17 Third baseman who made a diving catch in the final out of the 2014 World Series: Pablo _ _ _

18 Outfielder who made "The Catch" in Game 7 of the 1991 World Series: Kirby _ _ _

DOWN

2 Shortstop who made a behind-the-back catch in the 2005 ALDS: Orlando _ _ _

5 Second baseman who made a spectacular diving catch in the 2015 ALDS: José _ _ _

7 Third baseman who made a barehanded catch in the 2015 ALDS: Josh _ _ _

9 Center fielder known for his spectacular diving catches throughout his career: Jim _ _ _

11 Shortstop who made a diving stop and throw from his knees in the 2016 World Series: Addison _ _ _

12 Center fielder who robbed a home run in the 2006 NLCS: Endy _ _ _

15 Second baseman known for his "Spider-Man" catch in the 2006 NLCS: Jeff _ _ _

16 Third baseman known for his diving catch in the 2002 ALCS: Aaron _ _ _

41- Comeback Wins

ACROSS

2 Team that made a historic comeback from a 3-0 deficit to win the 2004 ALCS: Boston ___

4 Player who hit a walk-off home run in the 2019 ALCS Game 6 to extend the series for the Houston Astros: José ___

6 In Game 5 of the 2017 World Series, this team came back from a five-run deficit in the ninth inning to win in extra innings

7 In Game 6 of the 1986 World Series, the New York Mets made a famous comeback win by scoring three runs in the bottom of the ___th inning

10 Team that came back from a 3-1 deficit to win the 2016 World Series

11 Team that made a memorable comeback from a 2-0 series deficit to win the 1996 World Series

DOWN

1 Player who hit a game-tying home run in the 2016 World Series Game 7, contributing to the Chicago Cubs' historic comeback win: Rajai ___

2 Player who hit a walk-off home run in Game 7 of the 1997 World Series to help the Florida Marlins win their first championship: Edgar ___

3 In Game 4 of the 2001 World Series, this team scored two runs in the bottom of the ninth to tie the game and eventually win in extra innings

5 In the 2019 NLCS, the Washington Nationals overcame a ___-run deficit to win Game 5 against the Los Angeles Dodgers

7 In Game 7 of the 1991 World Series, this team came back from a 3-2 deficit in the bottom of the 10th inning to win on a walk-off single: Minnesota ___

8 Player who hit a game-tying three-run homer in Game 5 of the 2015 NLDS, sparking the Kansas City Royals' comeback against the Houston Astros: Alex ___

9 In 2011, the team overcame a 10.5-game deficit in September to clinch a playoff spot on the final day of the season: Tampa Bay ___

42- Playoff Push

ACROSS

3 During the September playoff push in 2019, this pitcher recorded a 1.46 ERA with 42 strikeouts for the Houston Astros: Justin ___

5 In 2019, this team went on a remarkable September playoff push to secure the AL Wild Card spot

6 This outfielder played a pivotal role in the 2018 playoff push for the Milwaukee Brewers, hitting .364 with 15 home runs in September: Christian ___

8 During the September playoff push in 2007, this pitcher recorded a 1.69 ERA with 54 strikeouts for the New York Mets: Johan ___

11 This outfielder's hot bat during the September playoff push in 2016 helped the Toronto Blue Jays secure a postseason berth: Jose ___

12 This outfielder was instrumental in the September playoff push of the 2007 Colorado Rockies, hitting .340 with 11 home runs

13 This pitcher was dominant during the September playoff push in 2013, recording a 1.09 ERA with 59 strikeouts for the Los Angeles Dodgers: Clayton ___

DOWN

1 In 2004, this team went on a memorable September playoff push, overcoming a significant deficit to clinch the AL Wild Card

2 This player led the September playoff push of the 2016 Detroit Tigers with a .404 batting average and 8 home runs: Miguel ___

4 This infielder's clutch hitting during the September playoff push in 2014 helped the Kansas City Royals secure a postseason berth: Lorenzo ___

7 During the September playoff push in 2018, this pitcher recorded a 1.85 ERA with 50 strikeouts for the Chicago Cubs: Cole ___

9 This pitcher's dominant performance during the September playoff push in 2019 helped the Washington Nationals secure a postseason berth: Stephen ___

10 This team's dramatic September playoff push in 1993 saw them clinch the NL West division title on the final day of the regular season

11 This player had a remarkable performance during the September playoff push in 1995, hitting .417 with 13 home runs: Albert ___

43- Perfect Pitch

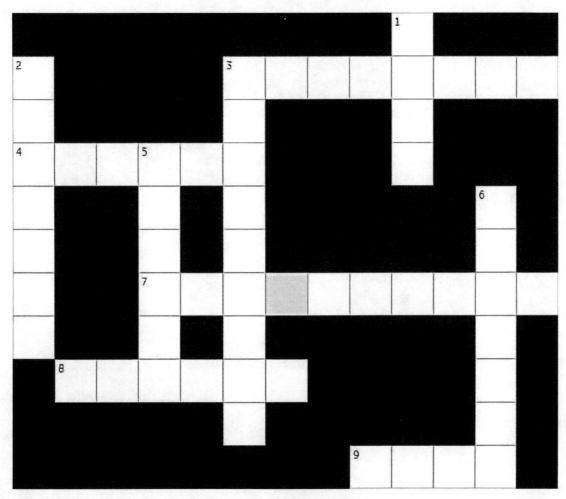

ACROSS

3 In 2010, this pitcher for the Philadelphia Phillies threw a perfect game against the Florida Marlins

4 The most recent perfect game in MLB history was thrown by this pitcher for the Chicago White Sox in 2012: Philip _ _ _

7 The only pitcher to throw a perfect game in World Series history, accomplishing the feat for the New York Yankees in 1956

8 This Hall of Famer threw a perfect game for the Oakland Athletics against the Minnesota Twins on May 8, 1968: James "Catfish" _ _ _

9 This Hall of Famer threw a perfect game for the New York Yankees against the Cleveland Indians on May 17, 1998: David _ _ _

DOWN

1 The first perfect game in modern MLB history was thrown by this pitcher for the Providence Grays on June 12, 1880: John _ _ _

2 This pitcher for the Arizona Diamondbacks threw a perfect game against the San Diego Padres on May 18, 2004: Randy _ _ _

3 This left-handed pitcher for the Seattle Mariners threw a perfect game against the Tampa Bay Rays on August 15, 2012: Félix

_ _ _

5 On May 29, 2010, this pitcher for the Oakland Athletics threw a perfect game against the Tampa Bay Rays: Dallas _ _ _

6 On July 23, 2009, this pitcher for the Chicago White Sox threw a perfect game against the Tampa Bay Rays: Mark _ _ _

44- Bat Flip

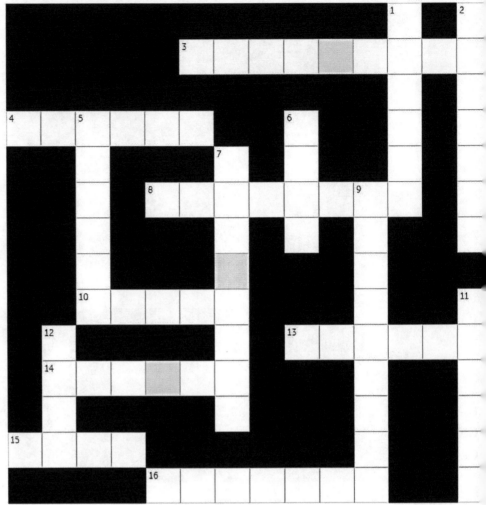

ACROSS

3 In Game 6 of the 2019 World Series, this Nationals outfielder's bat flip after a crucial home run helped propel his team to victory over the Houston Astros

4 This outfielder's bat flip after hitting a home run in Game 7 of the 2016 World Series added to the excitement of the Chicago Cubs' historic victory: Dexter ___

8 In Game 5 of the 2015 ALDS, this player's bat flip after hitting a decisive three-run homer sparked controversy and excitement

10 In the 2020 NL Wild Card Series, this Padres infielder's bat flip following a home run against the St. Louis Cardinals drew attention and debate: Fernando ___ Jr.

13 During the 2017 World Baseball Classic, this Venezuelan infielder's bat flip after a home run showcased his enthusiasm for the game

14 This Korean outfielder's bat flip during the 2015 Korean Series showcased his celebration style after hitting a walk-off home run: Lee ___

15 This Dominican outfielder's bat flip in the 2013 World Baseball Classic became legendary, reflecting his passion for the game: Nelson ___

16 This MLB infielder's bat flip during Game 3 of the 2018 NLCS, after hitting a home run against the Milwaukee Brewers, became a memorable moment in postseason history: Manny ___

DOWN

1 During the 2017 World Baseball Classic, this Puerto Rican outfielder's bat flip following a home run against the Dominican Republic became a highlight of the tournament: Carlos ___

2 This MLB outfielder's bat flip in Game 4 of the 2021 ALCS, after hitting a go-ahead home run against the Boston Red Sox, became a memorable moment: Eddie ___

5 This player's bat spike after hitting a home run in the 1986 World Series became an iconic image: Glend ___

6 This MLB infielder's bat flip during a regular-season game in 2016 drew attention for its style and swagger: Yasiel ___

7 This Korean baseball player's bat flip became legendary during the 2015 Korean Series, displaying his exuberance after hitting a game-winning home run: Choi ___

9 This Japanese outfielder's bat flip became famous during the 2017 World Baseball Classic, showcasing his flair for the dramatic after hitting a home run: Yoshitomo __

11 During Game 2 of the 2018 NLCS, this Brewers outfielder unleashed an epic bat flip after hitting a crucial home run: Christian ___

12 During the 2015 ALDS, this Rangers infielder's bat flip after hitting a go-ahead home run in Game 5 against the Toronto Blue Jays generated excitement and controversy: Rougned ___

45- Rival Teams

ACROSS

2 This rivalry between the Detroit Tigers and the Cleveland Guardians dates back to the early 20th century

6 The Freeway Series is a rivalry between the Los Angeles Angels and this other Los Angeles team: Angels vs. _ _ _

9 The Beltway Series is a rivalry between the Washington Nationals and this nearby American League team: Nationals vs. _ _ _

13 This intense rivalry in the National League Central division pits the Chicago Cubs against the Milwaukee _ _ _

14 The Subway Series is a fierce interleague rivalry between the New York Mets and this other New York team: Mets vs. _ _ _

15 The Lone Star Series is a rivalry between the Texas Rangers and this other Texas team: Rangers vs. _ _ _

DOWN

1 The Cross-town Classic is a rivalry between the Chicago Cubs and this other Chicago team: Cubs vs. _ _ _

3 The Lone Star Series is a rivalry between the Texas Rangers and this other Texas team: Rangers vs. _ _ _

4 This rivalry between the New York Yankees and the Toronto _ _ _ has intensified in the American League East division

5 The I-70 Series is a rivalry between the St. Louis Cardinals and this Missouri team: Cardinals vs. _ _ _

7 The Turnpike Series is a rivalry between the Philadelphia Phillies and this other Pennsylvania team: Phillies vs. _ _ _

8 This heated rivalry in the National League East division features the Philadelphia Phillies and the Atlanta _ _ _

10 The Battle of Ohio is a rivalry between the Cincinnati Reds and this other Ohio team: Reds vs. _ _ _

11 This interstate rivalry in the National League Central division features: Cardinals vs. _ _ _

12 This historic rivalry in the National League Central division features the Chicago Cubs and the Cincinnati _ _ _

46- Division Champs

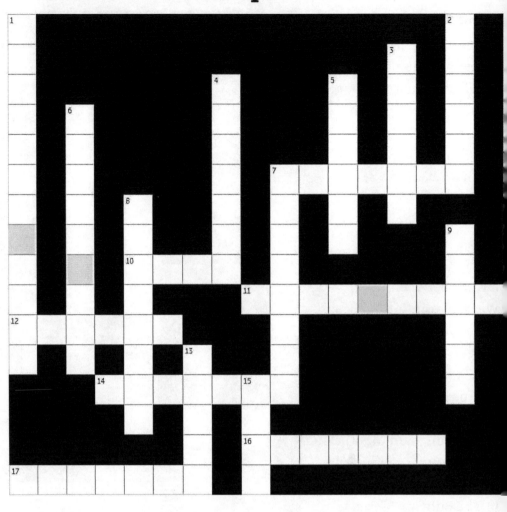

ACROSS

7 Champions of the National League East division in the 1975 MLB season

10 Winners of the American League East division in the 2020 MLB season: Tampa Bay _ _ _

11 Champions of the American League East division in the 1985 MLB season

12 Team that clinched the American League West division title in the 1944 MLB season: St. Louis _ _ _

14 Team that clinched the National League Central division title in the 2021 MLB season: Milwaukee _ _ _

16 Champions of the National League West division in the 2020 MLB season

17 Winners of the 2023 World Series

DOWN

1 Winners of the National League Central division in the 1998 MLB season

2 Winners of the National League East division in the 2020 MLB season

3 Champions of the National League West division in the 2021 MLB season

4 Champions of the American League East division in the 2000 MLB season

5 Champions of the American League West division in the 2021 MLB season

6 Team that clinched the American League Central division title in the 2021 MLB season

7 Champions of the National League East division in the 1993 MLB season

8 Team that clinched the American League West division title in the 1995 MLB season

9 Team that clinched the American League West division title in the 1977 MLB season

13 Team that clinched the American League Central division title in the 2020 MLB season

15 Winners of the National League East division in the 193 MLB season: Cincinnati _ _ _

47- World Series MVP

ACROSS

1 This pitcher won World Series MVP in 2019, earning two wins and a save to help his team secure the championship: Stephen _ _ _

3 In 1988, this outfielder won World Series MVP after his memorable walk-off home run in Game 1: Kirk _ _ _

5 In 1975, this outfielder was named World Series MVP after batting .615 with a memorable Game 6 home run: Pete _ _ _

8 World Series MVP in 2004, known for his clutch hitting and leadership during his team's historic comeback: Manny _ _ _

9 This pitcher won World Series MVP in 2014, delivering two dominant starts to help his team secure the championship: Madison _ _ _

12 World Series MVP in 2018, hitting .333 with three home runs and eight RBIs to lead his team to victory: Steve _ _ _

13 This pitcher won World Series MVP in 2017, recording two wins and a save in dominant performances: George _ _ _

DOWN

2 World Series MVP in 2010, hitting .429 with two home runs and six RBIs to lead his team to victory: Édgar _ _ _

4 World Series MVP in 2021, helping his team secure the championship with dominant pitching performances: Jorge _ _

6 In 1999, this pitcher was named World Series MVP after leading his team to a title with two wins and a save: Mariano _ _ _

7 World Series MVP in 2016, playing a pivotal role in breaking a long championship drought for his team: Ben _ _ _

10 In 1991, this pitcher earned World Series MVP honors after winning two games and saving another to help his team win the championship: Jack _ _ _

11 World Series MVP in 1978, leading his team to victory with stellar pitching performances: Bucky _ _ _

48- All-Star Game

ACROSS

1 The venue for the 2021 MLB All-Star Game: ___ Field

4 The first MLB All-Star Game was held at this ballpark: ___ Park

7 The player who holds the record for the most All-Star Game appearances with 25: Hank ___

10 The youngest player to appear in an MLB All-Star Game at 19 years old: Dwight ___

11 The city that hosted the 2019 MLB All-Star Game: ___, Ohio

13 The All-Star Game MVP award is named after this legendary Yankees player: Ted ___

14 The player who won the All-Star Game MVP award in 2021: Vladimir ___ Jr.

DOWN

2 The American League has won this many consecutive All-Star Games from 2013 to 2019

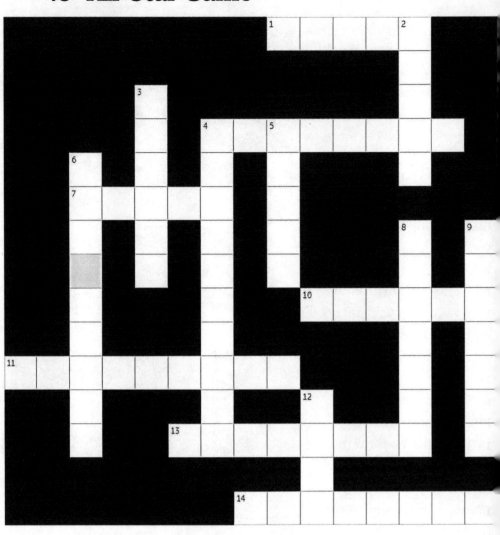

3 The number of players typically selected from each league to participate in the MLB All-Star Game

4 The city that hosted the 2015 MLB All-Star Game: ___, Ohio

5 The city that hosted the 2017 MLB All-Star Game: ___, Florida

6 The city that hosted the 2016 MLB All-Star Game: ___ California

8 The team that has won the most All-Star Games in National League history

9 The team that has won the most All-Star Games in American League history

12 The number of innings typically played in the MLB All-Star Game

49- Spring Fever

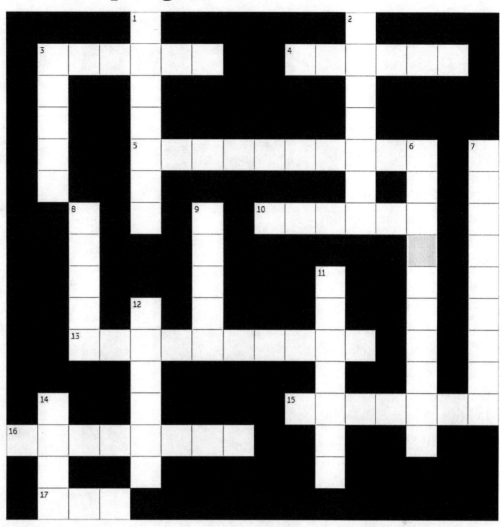

ACROSS

3 The period during ___ training when players focus on conditioning and skill development

4 The team that holds the record for the highest spring training winning percentage

5 The term for the informal games played between MLB teams during spring training

10 Spring training serves as a precursor to the MLB ___

13 Spring training games are also known as ___ League

15 The team that holds the record for the most spring training championships

16 Spring training typically begins in this month

17 The length of spring training, lasting approximately ___ weeks

DOWN

1 The number of teams in the Cactus League

2 The team that holds the record for the most spring training losses

3 Spring training often features games against college or international ___ teams

6 The term for players who are invited to spring training but are not on the team's regular roster

7 Spring training games often take place in these types of stadiums

8 Spring training provides an opportunity for teams to evaluate and develop ___ talent

9 Spring training games are an opportunity for fans to get ___ to the upcoming season

11 The team that won the first-ever spring training game in MLB history: ___ White Stockings

12 The location of the Arizona-based MLB teams' spring training facilities: ___ League

14 The team that holds the record for the most consecutive wins in spring training

50- Bat Speed

ACROSS

2 Measurement of how quickly a batter can move the bat through the hitting zone: _ _ _ Speed

5 A common training method to improve bat speed is using a _ _ _ bat

6 The point of contact between the bat and the ball is crucial for maximizing bat speed: _ _ _ Zone

7 Bat speed is measured in _ _ _ per hour (mph)

9 Fast-twitch muscle fibers are important for generating _ _ _ bat speed

13 Bat speed is crucial for driving the ball with _ _ _

14 A high bat speed can result in more _ _ _ contact

15 A bat with a larger _ _ _ can help increase bat speed by providing a larger hitting surface

DOWN

1 The speed at which the ball approaches the bat also affects the resulting bat speed: _ _ _ Velocity

3 This type of bat is often associated with faster bat speed due to its lighter weight: _ _ _ Bat

4 This type of swing aims to maximize bat speed by focusing on quick hands and a short, compact swing: _ _ _ Swing

8 The rotational movement of the hips and _ _ _ contributes to bat speed

10 Increasing bat speed often involves improving _ _ _ strength

11 A quick _ _ _ can significantly increase a batter's bat speed

12 A longer bat can generate more _ _ _ when swung with the same speed

51- Home Run Derby

ACROSS

6 The format of the Home Run Derby often features a set time limit per _ _ _

7 The participant who hits the most home runs overall in the Home Run Derby wins the _ _ _

10 This MLB player won the Home Run Derby in 2007, setting a record with 28 home runs in a single round: _ _ _ Fielder

11 This MLB player won the inaugural Home Run Derby in 1985: _ _ _ McGwire

14 The participant who hits the most home runs in each round advances to the _ _ _ round

16 This MLB player won the 2021 Home Run Derby, becoming the first from his country to win: Pete _ _ _

DOWN

1 This MLB player won the Home Run Derby three consecutive times from 2015 to 2017: _ _ _ Stanton

2 The Home Run Derby is typically held during the MLB _ _ _ Break

3 The participant who hits the fewest home runs in each round is eliminated from _ _ _

4 This MLB player won the Home Run Derby in 2005 and 2006, becoming the first to win consecutive titles: Bobby _ _ _

5 This MLB player won the Home Run Derby in 2019, hitting a total of 91 home runs across three rounds: _ _ _ Alonso

8 The Home Run Derby typically features _ _ _ of the league's top power hitters

9 The Home Run Derby often features a _ _ _ round to determine the final matchup

12 This MLB player won the Home Run Derby in 1996, hitting a record 41 home runs: _ _ _ Griffey Jr.

13 The trophy awarded to the winner of the Home Run Derby is named after this legendary MLB player: _ _ _ Robinson

15 This MLB player won the Home Run Derby in 2008 and was known for his "bat flip" celebrations: _ _ _ Hamilton

52- Starting Pitcher

ACROSS

1 This MLB pitcher holds the record for the most career strikeouts: Nolan _ _ _

3 The pitcher who starts the game for the home team is called the _ _ _ pitcher

6 This MLB pitcher holds the record for the most career wins

7 A starting pitcher who excels in a particular game may be referred to as having a _ _ _ performance

10 The starting pitcher is often supported by a _ _ _ catcher

12 A starting pitcher aims to pitch deep into the game to give the bullpen _ _ _

13 The number of starting pitchers in a team's rotation varies, commonly between _ _ _ and five

14 This statistic measures the number of innings a pitcher completes per game on average: _ _ _ per Game

15 This statistic measures the ratio of strikeouts to walks for a pitcher: Strikeout-to-_ _ _ Ratio

17 This statistic measures a pitcher's effectiveness in preventing runs: Earned _ _ _

DOWN

2 The pitcher who starts the game for the visiting team is called the _ _ _ pitcher

4 The starting pitcher stands on this raised area of the field

5 This statistic measures a pitcher's ability to induce ground balls: Ground _ _ _ Rate

6 A starting pitcher typically throws this type of pitch with movement

8 A starting pitcher typically warms up in the _ _ _ before the game

9 A starting pitcher typically throws this type of pitch to begin the game: _ _ _ Ball

11 This Hall of Fame pitcher was known as "The Big Unit": Randy _ _ _

12 The starting pitcher's primary objective is to _ _ _ opposing batters

16 The pitcher who starts on Opening Day for a team is often considered the _ _ _ of the rotation

53- Relief Pitcher

ACROSS

1 This MLB pitcher holds the record for the most career relief appearances: Jesse _ _ _

4 This Hall of Fame relief pitcher was known as "The Sandman"

5 A relief pitcher who enters the game to finish it is said to _ _ _ the game

6 A relief pitcher is also commonly referred to as a _ _ _

8 This MLB pitcher holds the record for the most career saves: Mariano _ _ _

9 A relief pitcher who enters the game with runners on base and no outs is said to _ _ _ the fire

11 A relief pitcher who enters the game in a crucial situation may be called a _ _ _ reliever

13 The relief pitcher who enters the game to bridge the gap between the starter and the closer is called the _ _ _ reliever

14 A relief pitcher who enters the game to face only one batter is called a _ _ _ specialist

DOWN

2 The relief pitcher who enters the game in the ninth inning to preserve a narrow lead is called the _ _ _

3 This statistic measures the number of saves a relief pitcher has successfully completed: Save _ _ _

4 The role of a relief pitcher is to maintain the lead or _ _ _ the deficit

7 The relief pitcher who enters the game in the middle innings to provide length is called the _ _ _ pitcher

10 The pitcher who enters the game to replace the starting pitcher is called the _ _ _ pitcher

11 The role of a relief pitcher is to _ _ _ the opposing team's offense

12 This statistic measures the number of strikeouts a relief pitcher records per nine innings pitched: Strikeouts per _ _ _

54- Double Header

ACROSS

1 This MLB team famously played two consecutive double headers in 1920

4 A double header consists of two consecutive _ _ _ games

6 Double headers can be physically _ _ _ for players

10 Double headers are more commonly played in the early _ _ _ of the season

11 The length of games in a double header is typically reduced to _ _ _ innings

12 A double header is often scheduled when a previous game was _ _ _ out

13 Some teams offer discounted tickets for double headers as part of a _ _ _ promotion

DOWN

2 The first game of a double header is often referred to as the _ _ _ game

3 Double headers can be a _ _ _ for fans, allowing them to see two games in one day

5 The decision to schedule a double header is often made by the _ _ _

7 The second game of a double header is commonly known as the _ _ _ game

8 This term refers to playing two games in one day: Double _ _ _

9 In some cases, double headers may be scheduled to accommodate a team's _ _ _ schedule

10 A team may call up additional players from the _ _ _ to have fresh arms for a double header

55- Bullpen Closers

ACROSS

4 The pitcher who won the National League Reliever of the Year Award in 2021: Josh ___

5 This statistic measures the ratio of strikeouts to walks for a closer: Strikeout-to-___ Ratio

6 A closer with exceptional control and accuracy is said to have ___ command

9 The number of saves a closer has successfully completed is an important ___ of his effectiveness

11 A bullpen closer is often known for his ability to throw a devastating ___ pitch

13 The pitcher who holds the MLB record for the most consecutive save opportunities converted: Eric ___

15 A closer often relies on his ___ to deceive batters

17 A closer is often known for his ability to maintain ___ in high-pressure situations

18 A closer who consistently pitches well in non-save situations is known for his ___

DOWN

1 A closer with a high strikeout rate is said to have a ___ fastball

2 This MLB team's closer is known as "The Cuban Missile": Aroldis ___

3 The pitcher who enters the game in the ninth inning to secure the win for his team

4 This MLB pitcher won the Mariano Rivera AL Reliever of the Year Award in 2021: Liam ___

6 The term for the final pitch thrown by a closer to secure the win: Save ___

7 This MLB pitcher holds the record for the most career saves: Mariano ___

8 The pitcher who holds the record for the most saves in a single month: John ___

10 A closer who enters the game with a narrow lead is said to be pitching in a ___ situation

11 The pitcher who holds the record for the most saves in a single season by a rookie: Neftali ___

12 A closer's performance is often crucial in the ___ innings of a game

14 This MLB team's closer is known as "The Bear": Craig ___

16 A closer's job is to shut down the opposing team's offense and ___ the win for his team

56- Batting Stance

ACROSS

1 A balanced batting stance helps a batter _ _ _ his weight

3 A batting stance may be adjusted based on a batter's _ _ _ or weaknesses

5 This MLB player's exaggerated leg kick was a signature of his batting stance: Gary _ _ _

9 A batting stance is often influenced by a batter's _ _ _

11 A square batting stance involves positioning the feet _ _ _ to the plate

13 A batter's stance may change depending on the game _ _ _

15 This MLB player had a unique "toe-tap" batting stance: _ _ _ Pujols

16 A batting stance is a key component of a batter's _ _ _

17 This MLB player's batting stance was famously imitated by "The Simpsons" character Darryl _ _ _

DOWN

2 The way a batter stands at home plate before swinging: _ _ _ Stance

4 This Hall of Fame slugger had a distinctive wide-legged batting stance: Willie _ _ _

5 The position of the hands in a batting stance can affect a batter's _ _ _

6 A staggered stance involves positioning the feet at _ _ _ heights

7 The timing of a batter's stride in his batting stance is crucial for _ _ _ timing

8 A batting stance can be adjusted based on the pitcher's _ _ _

10 The width of a batter's stance can affect his _ _ _ to pitches

12 A closed batting stance involves turning the front foot _ _ _ the plate

14 A batter may adopt a crouched stance to _ _ _ the strike zone

57- Pitching Motion

ACROSS

2 The sequence of movements a pitcher makes to throw the ball: ___ Motion

4 This MLB pitcher's "inverted W" caused concern among pitching mechanics experts: Mark ___

8 This Hall of Fame pitcher's "leg kick" was a signature of his pitching motion: Juan ___

9 A herky-jerky pitching motion can be difficult for batters to ___

12 A mechanical flaw in a pitcher's motion can lead to decreased ___

13 A balanced pitching motion allows a pitcher to maintain ___

14 A pitching motion can vary depending on the type of ___ being thrown

DOWN

1 A compact pitching motion can help reduce the risk of ___

2 The drive leg plays a crucial role in generating ___ in a pitcher's motion

3 This MLB pitcher's "knee-buckling" curveball was a product of his unique pitching motion: Sandy ___

5 A fluid pitching motion allows a pitcher to generate maximum ___

6 This MLB pitcher's "crossfire" delivery made him difficult to hit: Don ___

7 A consistent release point helps a pitcher maintain ___

9 A deceptive pitching motion can make it difficult for batters to ___ the ball

10 This MLB pitcher had a unique "whirl and twirl" pitching motion: Luis ___

11 A smooth pitching motion can help reduce stress on the pitcher's ___

58- Base Stealer

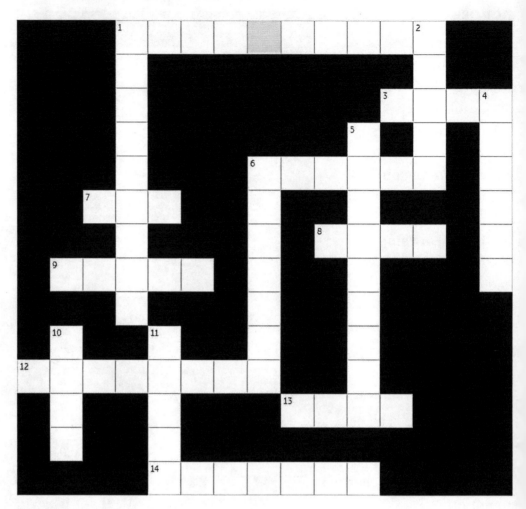

ACROSS

1 A base stealer may use a _ _ _ slide to avoid the tag at the base

3 A base stealer relies on quick _ _ _ to beat the throw to the next base

6 A base stealer's success often depends on his ability to _ _ _ the pitcher's attention

7 A base stealer often studies the _ _ _ of the catcher to time their steal

8 This Hall of Fame outfielder was known as "The Georgia Peach" and was a prolific base stealer: Ty _ _ _

9 This MLB player holds the record for the most consecutive seasons leading the league in stolen bases: Lou _ _ _

12 A base stealer with exceptional speed may attempt to steal _ _ _ bases

13 This MLB player was known as "The Say Hey Kid" and was a skilled base stealer: Willie _ _ _

14 A player known for his speed and ability to steal bases: Base _ _ _

DOWN

1 This MLB player holds the record for the most stolen bases in a single season: Rickey _ _ _

2 The element of surprise is crucial for a successful base _ _ _

4 The ability to anticipate the pitcher's move is known as _ _ _

5 A base stealer may use a _ _ _ lead to get a jump on the pitcher

6 A base stealer may attempt to _ _ _ the pitcher by drawing a throw to the base

10 A base stealer's ability to get a good _ _ _ is crucial for a successful steal

11 This MLB player was known as "The Man of Steal" and holds the record for the most stolen bases in a single game: Maury _ _ _

59- Run Batted In

ACROSS

1 A batter who drives in a run without hitting the ball is credited with a ___ RBI

4 A batter who excels at driving in runs is often referred to as a "run ___"

7 A batter who consistently drives in runs is an important asset to his team's ___

9 This MLB player was known as "Mr. October" and was a clutch performer with runners in scoring position: Reggie ___

11 A batter who hits a double with two runners on base is credited with ___ RBIs

12 A batter who consistently delivers in clutch situations is known for his clutch ___

13 This MLB player holds the record for the most career runs batted in: Hank ___

14 The number of runners on base when a batter records a run batted in is referred to as ___

15 This MLB player holds the record for the most RBIs in a single season with 191: Hack ___

DOWN

2 A batter who hits a home run with the bases loaded is credited with ___ RBIs

3 The statistic for runs batted in is often used to measure a batter's ___

5 A statistic that measures a batter's effectiveness in producing runs: ___ Batted In

6 The number of RBIs a batter records in a single game is referred to as his ___ total

8 A batter's ability to drive in runs often depends on his ___ in the lineup

10 This MLB player led the league in runs batted in for seven consecutive seasons from 1998 to 2004: Alex ___

60- Leadoff Batter

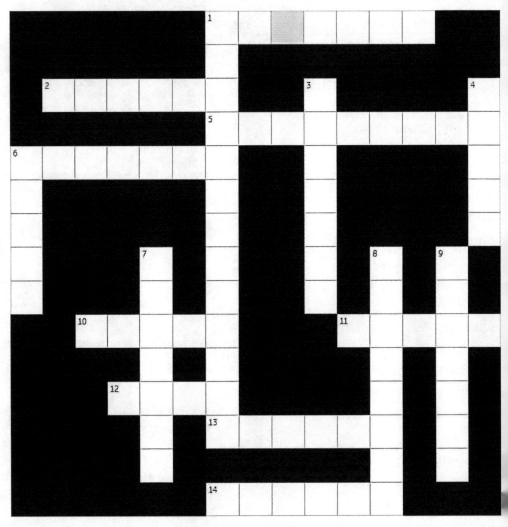

ACROSS

1 The ability to draw walks and work deep counts is important for a leadoff batter's _ _ _

2 The leadoff batter's performance often influences the rest of the

_ _ _

5 A leadoff batter who consistently gets on base is known as a _ _ _ catalyst

6 A leadoff batter may be tasked with working the count to tire out the opposing _ _ _

10 A leadoff batter's primary role is to get on base and _ _ _ the inning

11 A leadoff batter with power can provide an _ _ _ spark

12 This MLB player holds the record for the most career leadoff hits: Pete

_ _ _

13 This MLB player was known for his unconventional batting stance and leadoff hitting: Ichiro _ _ _

14 The leadoff batter sets the tone for the _ _ _

DOWN

1 The leadoff batter is often tasked with setting up scoring _ _ _ for the rest of the lineup

3 A leadoff batter with exceptional speed can put pressure on the _ _ _

4 This Hall of Fame shortstop was known for his leadoff hitting and base-stealing prowess: _ _ _ Jeter

6 A leadoff batter who hits for power is known as a _ _ _ threat

7 The first batter in the batting order is known as the

_ _ _

8 The leadoff batter often faces the opposing team's _ _ _ pitcher

9 This MLB player was known as "The Ignitor" for his leadoff hitting: Paul _ _ _

61- Game Winning Run

ACROSS

5 This MLB player scored the game-winning run in Game 7 of the 1997 World Series for the Florida Marlins: Edgar _ _ _

7 This MLB player hit the game-winning home run in Game 7 of the 1962 World Series: Ralph _ _ _

8 A game-winning run can come from a _ _ _ hit, sacrifice fly, or walk-off home run

9 The player who delivers the game-winning hit is often remembered as a _ _ _

10 The game-winning run can secure a _ _ _ victory for a team

13 A game-winning run can be scored in _ _ _ situations

15 This MLB player scored the game-winning run in the 1996 World Series for the New York Yankees: Derek _ _ _

16 This MLB player hit the game-winning home run in Game 7 of the 1960 World Series: Bill _ _ _

DOWN

1 The run that decides the outcome of the game is known as the game _ _ _ run

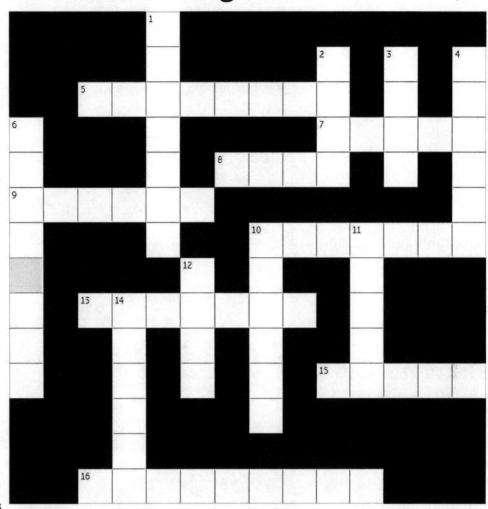

2 The game-winning run is typically scored in the _ _ _ inning

3 A player who scores the game-winning run is often hailed as the _ _ _

4 The player who crosses home plate to score the game-winning run is often greeted with a _ _ _ celebration

6 The celebration after scoring the game-winning run is often referred to as a _ _ _

10 A player who consistently delivers game-winning runs is known for his _ _ _

11 A game-winning run can be scored in _ _ _ situations

12 This MLB player hit the game-winning home run in Game 6 of the 1975 World Series: Carlton _ _ _

14 This MLB player scored the game-winning run in Game 7 of the 2016 World Series for the Chicago Cubs: Albert _ _ _

62- Pitching Duel

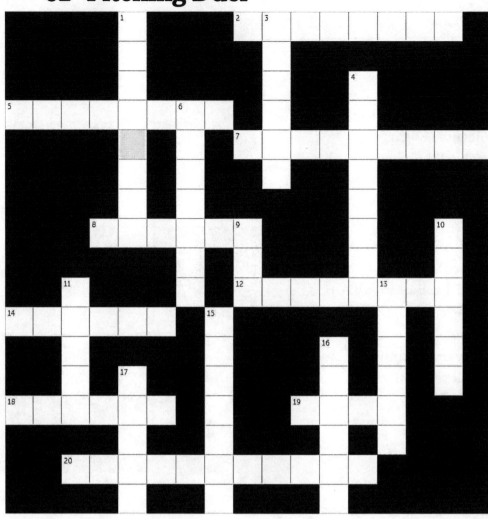

ACROSS

2 A pitching duel can be a battle of _ _ _ and wits between two skilled pitchers

5 The tension of a pitching duel often leads to heightened _ _ _

7 This MLB pitcher threw a perfect game in a memorable 2012 pitching duel against the Tampa Bay Rays: Felix _ _ _

8 The excitement of a pitching duel often builds with each _ _ _

12 This MLB pitcher threw a perfect game in a famous 1965 pitching duel against Sandy Koufax: Juan _ _ _

14 The winner of a pitching duel is often decided by the team that _ _ _ first

18 This MLB pitcher threw a no-hitter in a memorable 1959 pitching duel against the Milwaukee Braves: Harvey _ _ _

19 A game characterized by exceptional pitching performances from both starting pitchers: Pitching _ _ _

20 A pitching duel can be a showcase of _ _ _ pitching talent

DOWN

1 A pitching duel can be decided by a late-game _ _ _

3 The anticipation of a pitching duel often leads to increased _ _ _ sales

4 A pitching duel can captivate fans with its _ _ _ intensity

6 A pitching duel often results in a low _ _ _ game

9 The term for a game in which both starting pitchers dominate and allow few hits: _ _ _ game

10 This Hall of Fame pitcher was involved in many legendary pitching duels during his career with the Baltimore Orioles: Jim _ _ _

11 A pitching duel can showcase the importance of _ _ _ defense

13 This MLB pitcher threw a no-hitter in a memorable 2015 pitching duel against the Detroit Tigers: Cole _ _ _

15 A pitching duel can test a team's _ _ _ to manufacture runs

16 This Hall of Fame pitcher was known for his involvement in several memorable pitching duels during his career with the Los Angeles Dodgers

17 The outcome of a pitching duel often hinges on a key _ _ _ or play

63- Batting Gloves

ACROSS

4 The material used in modern batting gloves to provide grip and durability: Synthetic ___

6 This MLB player is known for wearing custom-designed batting gloves with his nickname: Bryce ___

8 The color of batting gloves is often coordinated with a player's team ___

9 The design of batting gloves has evolved over time to improve ___ and performance

10 Batting gloves are designed to enhance a batter's ___ on the bat

12 Some batting gloves feature ___ on the fingertips for added grip

15 Protective gear worn by batters to improve grip and reduce vibration: Batting ___

17 The use of batting gloves has become common among players at all levels of ___

18 This MLB player is known for wearing batting gloves with a unique lizard skin pattern: Jose ___

DOWN

1 This MLB player is known for wearing batting gloves with his logo prominently displayed: Derek ___

2 The use of batting gloves is often a matter of ___ for individual players

3 Some batting gloves feature ___ padding on the back of the hand for added protection

5 These accessories are sometimes worn underneath batting gloves for added warmth in cold weather: ___ liners

7 Batting gloves are an essential part of a batter's ___ gear

11 These parts of the batting gloves provide additional protection for the hands: ___ pads

13 Batting gloves are designed to reduce the ___ from impact when hitting the ball

14 Some batting gloves feature ___ inserts for added comfort and protection

16 These features on batting gloves help secure them to the hands: Velcro ___

64- Power Hitter

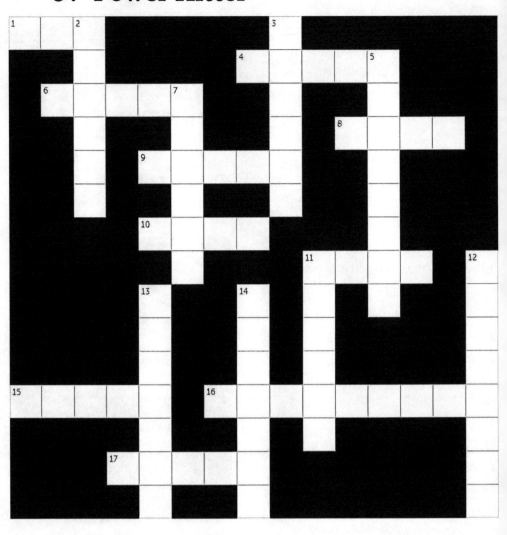

ACROSS

1 A power hitter's ability to drive the ball deep into the outfield is known as _ _ _ power

4 This MLB player holds the record for the most career home runs: Barry _ _ _

6 The term "tape-measure _ _ _" is often used to describe long home runs

8 This Hall of Famer was known as "The Sultan of Swat" for his power hitting: Babe _ _ _

9 This MLB player hit 73 home runs in a single season, setting a record: Barry _ _ _

10 A power hitter's ability to hit home runs with _ _ _ runners on base is valuable

11 This MLB player hit over 600 home runs in his career and was known as "Hammerin' _ _ _"

15 A power hitter's swing may produce a distinctive _ _ _ sound when making contact

16 A power hitter's performance is often measured by their _ _ _ statistics

17 A power hitter often generates a lot of _ _ _ when making contact with the ball

DOWN

2 A power hitter may be intentionally _ _ _ by opposing pitchers to avoid giving up home runs

3 A power hitter's ability to hit home runs can change the _ _ _ of a game

5 A power hitter may have a high _ _ _ percentage due to their ability to hit home runs

7 This MLB player was known as "The Big Hurt" for his power hitting: Frank _ _ _

11 A baseball player known for their ability to hit for extra bases and home runs: Power _ _ _

12 A power hitter's swing is often characterized by its _ _ _ and aggression

13 This MLB player was known as "Mr. October" for his clutch power hitting: Reggie _ _ _

14 This MLB player was known as "The Kid" for his prodigious power hitting: Ken _ _ _

65- Fastball Pitch

ACROSS

3 This MLB pitcher was known for his devastating cut fastball: Mariano _ _ _

5 A fastball thrown high in the strike zone is often called a _ _ _ fastball

7 A pitcher's fastball can be complemented by secondary pitches such as a _ _ _ or changeup

12 A well-located fastball can be an effective _ _ _ pitch

13 The velocity of a pitcher's fastball is often measured in _ _ _ per hour (mph)

14 This MLB pitcher holds the record for the fastest recorded fastball, clocking in at 105.1 mph: Aroldis _ _ _

16 A type of pitch known for its high velocity and minimal movement: _ _ _ pitch

DOWN

1 A pitcher's ability to change speeds on his fastball can keep hitters _ _ _

2 The release point of a fastball is crucial for _ _ _ control

4 The grip for a fastball typically involves holding the ball with the _ _ _ and middle fingers

6 A pitcher who relies heavily on his fastball is often referred to as a _ _ _ pitcher

8 A pitcher's fastball can be an effective weapon for _ _ _ batters

9 A fastball that tails away from a same-handed batter is known as a _ _ _ fastball

10 This MLB pitcher was known for his "rising" fastball that seemed to defy gravity: Roger _ _ _

11 This MLB pitcher was known for his overpowering fastball, often reaching over 100 mph: Nolan _ _ _

15 A pitcher's ability to throw a fastball with accuracy is crucial for success in the _ _ _

66- Curveball Pitch

ACROSS

4 A curveball can be an effective ___ pitch to get hitters to chase out of the strike zone

7 This MLB pitcher, known as "The Freak," had a unique delivery and a devastating curveball: Tim ___

10 A pitcher's arm ___ is crucial for generating the spin necessary for a curveball

11 A well-executed curveball can fool hitters with its ___ trajectory

13 A curveball is often used as a ___ pitch to keep hitters off balance

DOWN

1 A pitcher's ability to disguise his curveball can make it difficult for hitters to ___

2 This MLB pitcher was known for his knee-buckling curveball and famous eephus pitch: ___ Dickey

3 A type of pitch known for its sharp downward break: ___ pitch

4 The release point of a curveball is crucial for ___ control

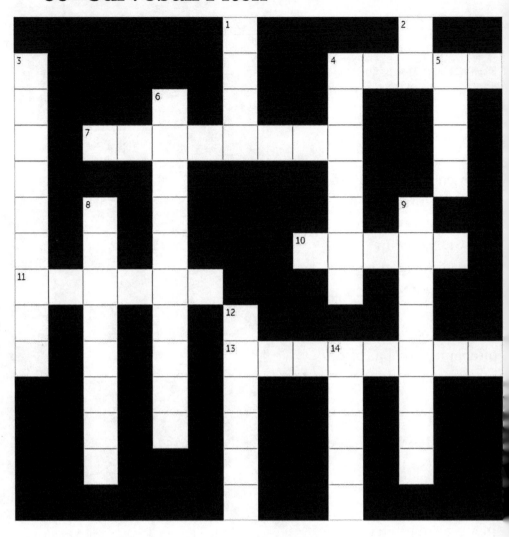

5 A curveball thrown with a slower speed can be referred to as a ___ curveball

6 The grip for a curveball typically involves placing the index and middle fingers along the seams and the thumb ___

8 A curveball that starts outside the strike zone and breaks into the zone is known as a ___ curveball

9 This MLB pitcher was known for his "slurve," a combination of a slider and curveball: Bert ___

12 This MLB pitcher, known as "Dr. K," was famous for his strikeout-inducing curveball: Dwight ___

14 A curveball thrown with a high spin rate can have a ___ break

67- Changeup Pitch

ACROSS

1 This MLB pitcher was known for his exceptional changeup, often compared to a butterfly: Pedro _ _ _

3 This MLB pitcher, known as "The Freak," had a devastating fastball-changeup combination: Tim _ _ _

4 A changeup thrown with a slower speed can be referred to as a _ _ _ changeup

5 This MLB pitcher was known for his circle changeup, a variation of the traditional grip: Johan _ _ _

9 This MLB pitcher, known as "Mad Dog," had an exceptional changeup that complemented his fastball: Greg _ _ _

11 A changeup is often used as a _ _ _ pitch to keep hitters off balance

14 A changeup that appears to be a fastball out of the pitcher's hand but slows down as it approaches the plate is called a _ _ _ changeup

15 A type of off-speed pitch designed to deceive hitters with a slower velocity: _ _ _ pitch

16 A changeup is an effective _ _ _ pitch to keep hitters guessing

DOWN

2 A changeup thrown with proper _ _ _ can mimic the arm action of a fastball

4 A well-located changeup can be an effective _ _ _ pitch

6 This MLB pitcher, known as "Big Train," was one of the earliest practitioners of the changeup: Walter _ _ _

7 A well-executed changeup can induce _ _ _ ground balls from hitters

8 The grip for a changeup typically involves holding the ball with the _ _ _ and ring fingers

10 The changeup is often considered a _ _ _ pitch for pitchers to master

12 A well-executed changeup can induce _ _ _ swings from hitters

13 A changeup is effective at disrupting a hitter's _ _ _ timing

68- Slider Pitch

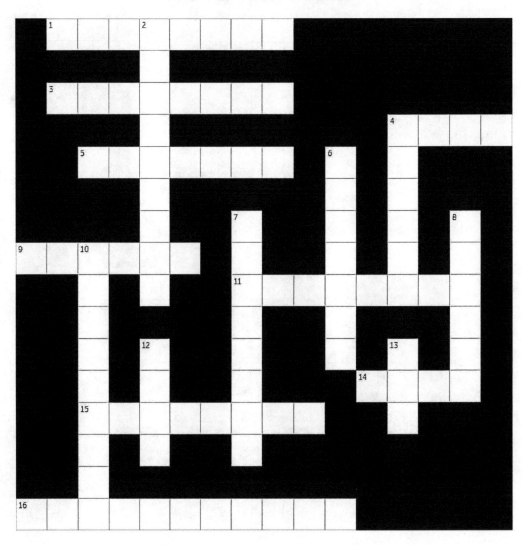

ACROSS

4 A slider is often used as a ___ pitch to keep hitters off balance

9 A type of breaking ball characterized by lateral movement: ___ pitch

10 This MLB pitcher, known as "The Terminator," was famous for his slider and intimidating presence on the mound: Bruce ___

11 A well-located slider can be an effective ___ pitch

DOWN

1 A slider is effective at inducing ___ ground balls from hitters

2 This MLB pitcher, known as "The Dark Knight," had a lethal fastball-slider combination: Matt ___

3 A slider is often considered a ___ pitch for pitchers to master

5 A slider that starts inside and breaks toward the outer part of the plate is known as a ___ slider

6 The slider is often used as a ___ pitch to complement a pitcher's fastball

7 This MLB pitcher was known for his devastating slider, often compared to a frisbee: Steve ___

8 The grip for a slider typically involves placing the index and middle fingers ___ together on one seam

69- Sinker Pitch

ACROSS

3 A sinker that starts in the strike zone and drops out of it is known as a ___ sinker

4 This MLB pitcher, known as "The Bulldog," was known for his sinker and fierce competitiveness: Orel ___

6 A well-executed sinker can be an effective pitch to induce ___ balls from hitters

7 A well-located sinker can be an effective ___ pitch

9 A well-executed sinker can be an effective pitch to induce hitters to chase ___ out of the strike zone

13 A well-executed sinker can induce ___ swings from hitters

DOWN

1 This MLB pitcher was known for his exceptional sinker, inducing countless double plays: Derek ___

2 The grip for a sinker is similar to that of a fastball, but the thumb is typically placed ___ on the ball

4 This MLB pitcher, known as "Doc," had a dominant sinker-slider combination: Roy ___

5 A well-executed sinker can be an effective pitch to induce ___ ground balls and double plays

7 A type of pitch known for its downward movement, inducing ground balls: ___ pitch

8 This MLB pitcher was known for his heavy sinker and durability, pitching well into his 40s: Bartolo ___

10 The movement of a sinker can vary depending on a pitcher's arm ___ and release point

11 This MLB pitcher, known as "The Sinkerballer," relied heavily on his sinking fastball: Brandon ___

12 A sinker can be an effective ___ pitch to induce double plays

70- Sacrifice Bunt

ACROSS

4 In sacrifice bunt situations, the batter often adopts a ___ stance to ensure better control over the bunt.

5 This MLB team is often associated with small-ball tactics, including frequent use of sacrifice bunts

7 A well-executed sacrifice bunt requires the batter to make ___ contact with the ball to avoid popping it up.

10 A sacrifice bunt can also be used to advance multiple baserunners, especially in situations where a team is ___ on runs.

11 This MLB manager was known for his emphasis on fundamentals, including executing sacrifice bunts: Tony ___

13 A sacrifice bunt can be part of a team's ___ approach, focusing on generating runs through timely hitting and baserunning.

DOWN

1 This MLB team's success in the 1980s was attributed in part to their mastery of small-ball tactics, including sacrifice bunts

2 This MLB manager was famous for his aggressive small-ball tactics, including frequent use of the sacrifice bunt: Whitey ___

3 This MLB player holds the record for the most career sacrifice bunts: Eddie ___

4 A sacrifice bunt is often employed to move a baserunner from ___ to third base with fewer than two outs.

6 A strategic play in baseball where a batter intentionally taps the ball softly to advance a baserunner: ___ bunt

8 The sacrifice bunt can be an effective strategy to counteract a dominant ___ pitcher who is difficult to hit.

9 In sacrifice bunt situations, baserunners are often instructed to ___ from their base as soon as the pitcher begins their delivery.

12 This MLB player was known for his exceptional bunting skills and ability to execute sacrifice bunts: Pete ___

71- Walk-Off Hit

ACROSS

3 This MLB team's walk-off victory in Game 7 of the 2016 World Series ended a 108-year championship drought

4 This MLB manager, known for his analytical approach to the game, has led his teams to numerous walk-off victories using innovative strategies: AJ ___

6 The ___ Stadium in San Francisco witnessed numerous walk-off hits during its tenure as the home of the Giants.

9 This Hall of Fame manager led the Boston Red Sox to numerous walk-off victories during his tenure: Terry ___

11 This historic MLB ballpark, known for its ivy-covered outfield walls, has been the site of numerous walk-off victories for the Chicago Cubs: ___ Field

12 This MLB player, known for his colorful personality, has delivered walk-off hits while playing for multiple teams, including the "Curse-Breaking" Red Sox and the New York Yankees: Johnny ___

14 This MLB team's fans famously celebrated a walk-off win by launching "rally fries" onto the field

15 In 2016, this MLB player delivered one of the most dramatic walk-off hits in World Series history, helping his team come back from a 3-1 deficit to win the title: Rajai ___

16 This MLB manager, known for his fiery demeanor, has a knack for inspiring his team to come through with walk-off victories: Bobby ___

DOWN

1 Known for his powerful swing, this MLB player has delivered several memorable walk-off home runs, earning him the nickname "Big Mac"

2 This MLB coach is revered for his strategic prowess, often putting his players in a position to deliver walk-off heroics: Joe ___

5 This legendary New York Yankees shortstop was known for his clutch walk-off hits, including a famous one in his final game at Yankee Stadium

7 This MLB team's fans are known for their elaborate celebrations after walk-off hits, often involving themed costumes and props

8 This MLB coach, known for his expertise in hitting, has helped many players refine their skills, leading to numerous walk-off hits throughout his career: John ___

10 This MLB team's historic ballpark, built in 1912, has seen its fair share of walk-off hits, including many during its famous Green Monster era

13 This MLB team is famous for its "Miracle Mets" season, culminating in a walk-off victory in the 1969 World Series

72- Sacrifice Fly

ACROSS

2 The sacrifice fly is often employed in situations where a team needs to score a run, such as in late-game or _ _ _ situations

5 This historic MLB ballpark, home to the Philadelphia Phillies, has seen its fair share of sacrifice flies over the years: _ _ _ Park

7 A sacrifice fly can be part of a team's offensive _ _ _ approach, focusing on generating runs through timely hitting and baserunning

10 This MLB player holds the record for the most career sacrifice flies, displaying exceptional situational hitting skills: Eddie _ _ _

11 This MLB player, known for his clutch hitting, has delivered multiple walk-off sacrifice flies throughout his career: David _ _ _

13 A sacrifice fly occurs when a batter hits a ball deep enough to allow a baserunner to tag up and score a run, but not deep enough for the batter to reach _ _ _ base

14 This MLB team's historic ballpark, located in Chicago, has seen its fair share of sacrifice flies, including many hit by legends like Ernie Banks and Ryne Sandberg: _ _ _ Field

DOWN

1 This MLB team's manager is known for employing small-ball tactics, including the effective use of sacrifice flies

3 This MLB manager, known for his emphasis on fundamentals, often incorporates the sacrifice fly into his team's offensive strategy: Joe _ _ _

4 This MLB manager, known for his innovative approach to the game, has been successful in incorporating the sacrifice fly into his team's offensive playbook: _ _ _ Roberts

6 This MLB team's fans are known for their raucous celebrations after a sacrifice fly brings in a crucial run

8 A sacrifice fly is considered a productive out because it results in a run being scored, despite the batter being _ _ _ out

9 In a sacrifice fly situation, baserunners are often instructed to _ _ _ from their base as soon as the ball is caught by the outfielde

10 This MLB player, known for hi prowess in the batter's box, has delivered numerous clutch sacrifice flies throughout his career: _ _ _ Trout

12 A sacrifice fly can be particularly effective in late-gam situations, helping a team to _ _ _ deficit or extend a lead

73- Base on Balls

ACROSS

3 This MLB player, known for his keen eye at the plate, has led the league in walks multiple times throughout his career: Joey _ _ _

4 A base on balls, also known as a walk, is awarded to a batter who receives _ _ _ balls from the pitcher

6 In a base on balls situation, the pitcher is often looking to _ _ _ the strike zone, forcing the batter to swing at pitches out of their comfort zone

8 This MLB team's ballpark is known for its unique dimensions and is sometimes referred to as a "pitcher's park," leading to high walk rates

10 This MLB team's manager is known for his emphasis on patience at the plate, leading to high walk totals for his players

11 This MLB player, known for his power and patience at the plate, has a high career on-base percentage due in part to his ability to draw walks: _ _ _ Trout

12 A base on balls can be a crucial moment in a game, as it puts a baserunner on _ _ _ without requiring the batter to make contact.

14 The base on balls is a testament to a batter's _ _ _ eye and ability to recognize pitches in and out of the strike zone

16 A base on balls can be particularly valuable in close games, as it can lead to _ _ _ and potentially change the outcome of the game

DOWN

1 This MLB player holds the record for the most career walks, displaying exceptional plate discipline throughout his career: Barry _ _ _

2 This MLB coach, known for his expertise in hitting, often works with players to improve their plate discipline and ability to draw walks: _ _ _ Mallee

5 The base on balls is a valuable offensive tool, as it puts _ _ _ on base and increases the team's chances of scoring runs

7 A base on balls can be particularly frustrating for a pitcher, as it prolongs _ _ _ and increases the pitch count

9 This MLB team's fans are known for their "walk-up" chants, encouraging batters to be patient and draw base on balls

13 This MLB manager, known for his analytical approach to the game, emphasizes the importance of drawing walks as part of his team's offensive strategy: _ _ _ Hinch

15 This MLB team's fans are known for their elaborate celebrations after a player draws a base on balls to load the bases

74- Stolen Base

ACROSS

1 This MLB player holds the record for the most stolen bases in a single season, with an impressive 130 steals in 1982: Rickey _ _ _

6 This MLB player, known for his speed and agility, set the all-time record for career stolen bases with 1406 steals: Lou _ _ _

7 This MLB player, known for his aggressive baserunning, famously stole home plate in Game 1 of the 1955 World Series: Jackie _ _ _

9 This MLB team's fans are known for their excitement and enthusiasm when one of their players successfully steals a base

12 A successful stolen base can energize a team and _ _ _ momentum in their favor during a game

13 This historic MLB ballpark, located in Boston, has seen its fair share of stolen base attempts over the years: _ _ _ Park

14 This MLB team's aggressive baserunning tactics were instrumental in their success during the "Go-Go" era of the 1950s

15 In a stolen base attempt, the baserunner is often trying to _ _ _ the pitcher's delivery and the catcher's throw to the next base.

DOWN

2 A successful stolen base can put pressure on the opposing team's _ _ _ and disrupt their defensive strategy

3 A stolen base attempt requires the baserunner to have a quick _ _ _ and explosive first step to beat the throw to the next base

4 This MLB coach, known for his expertise in baserunning, has helped many players improve their technique and success rate when attempting stolen bases: _ _ _ Washington

5 This MLB team's manager is known for his aggressive baserunning strategy, often giving his players the green light to attempt stolen bases

8 This MLB manager, known for his innovative approach to the game, has incorporated analytics to optimize his team's stolen base success rate

10 A stolen base occurs when a baserunner successfully advances to the next base while the pitcher attempts to deliver a _ _ _ to home plate.

11 This MLB player, known for his speed on the basepaths, led the league in stolen bases for seven consecutive seasons from 1976 to 1982: Ron _ _ _

75- Caught Stealing

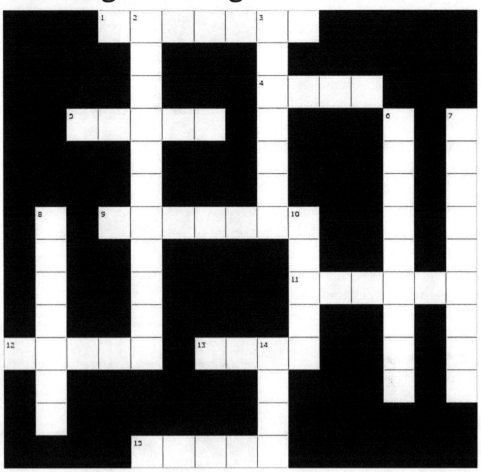

ACROSS

1 This MLB team's manager is known for his aggressive baserunning strategy, often leading to high numbers of stolen base attempts and occasional caught stealings

4 The caught stealing statistic is often used by teams and managers to evaluate a player's _ _ _ efficiency and baserunning decision-making

5 This MLB player, known for his combination of power and speed, has stolen numerous bases while also falling victim to caught stealings: Mike _ _ _

9 The caught stealing statistic is often included in a player's overall _ _ _ percentage, which measures their effectiveness on the basepaths

11 This MLB team's fans are known for their "steal signs" and cheers when their players successfully swipe bases, despite the occasional caught stealings

12 This MLB player, known for his lightning-fast speed, has led the league in stolen bases multiple times despite occasionally falling victim to caught stealings: _ _ _ Hamilton

13 In a caught stealing situation, the baserunner is often trying to time the pitcher's delivery and _ _ _ to maximize their chances of success

15 The caught stealing statistic is often used by teams to identify _ _ _ areas for improvement and adjust their baserunning strategies accordingly

DOWN

2 A caught stealing can be particularly costly in close games, as it can result in a lost _ _ _ and potentially change the outcome of the game

3 This MLB coach, known for his expertise in baserunning, often works with players to improve their technique and minimize the risk of caught stealings: Dave _ _ _

6 This MLB player holds the record for the most career stolen bases, demonstrating exceptional speed and baserunning prowess: Rickey _ _ _

7 A caught stealing can shift the momentum of a game in favor of the _ _ _ team, especially if it occurs in a crucial situation

8 In a caught stealing situation, the defensive team often celebrates the _ _ _ out, knowing they have successfully prevented a baserunner from advancing

10 A caught stealing can be a result of a _ _ _ defensive play, such as a well-executed throw from the catcher or a quick tag from the infielder

14 This MLB team's fans are known for their "basepath ballet" cheers, encouraging their players to be aggressive on the bases despite the occasional caught stealings

76- Pickoff Move

ACROSS

5 This MLB manager, known for his strategic acumen, often incorporates pickoff moves into his team's defensive game plan: Tony ___

6 This MLB pitcher is known for his deceptive pickoff move, which has caught many baserunners off guard: Andy ___

8 In a pickoff move, the pitcher often uses a quick ___ to try to catch the baserunner off balance and make a successful throw to the base

10 A pickoff move can be particularly effective in late-game situations, when every baserunner is ___ to the outcome of the game.

12 This MLB pitcher, known for his dominance on the mound, has recorded numerous pickoff moves throughout his career: Clayton ___

13 This MLB team's manager is known for his emphasis on defense, including teaching pitchers effective pickoff moves

DOWN

1 This MLB pitcher, known for his tall stature and deceptive delivery, has one of the best pickoff moves in the game: Jon ___

2 The pickoff move is an essential part of a pitcher's arsenal, helping to control the ___ and prevent stolen bases

3 This MLB team's fans are known for their "pickoff party" celebrations, where they cheer loudly after a successful pickoff move by their pitcher

4 This MLB pitcher, known for his crafty pitching style, has developed an effective pickoff move that has fooled many baserunners: Mark ___

7 This MLB team's fans are known for their loud cheers and chants when their pitcher successfully executes a pickoff move to nab a baserunner

8 The pickoff move is an example of a pitcher's ability to ___ the game and control the flow of play, even when not delivering a pitch

9 A successful pickoff move can be a result of a ___ throw by the pitcher, catching the baserunner off guard and leading to an easy out

11 A pickoff move is a quick throw by the pitcher to try to catch a baserunner off the ___ and tag them out

77- Double Steal

ACROSS

3 This MLB manager, known for his innovative strategies, has been successful in incorporating double steals into his team's offensive playbook: _ _ _ Roberts

4 This MLB team's fans are known for their elaborate celebrations after a successful double steal, often involving coordinated cheers and chants

6 This MLB team's fans are known for their cheers and chants when their team executes a successful double steal, often leading to runs scored

7 This MLB player is known for his speed on the basepaths, often executing double steals to create scoring opportunities for his team: Trea _ _ _

10 This MLB coach, known for his expertise in baserunning, often works with players to improve their technique and timing on double steals

11 A successful double steal requires communication and coordination among the baserunners, as well as trust in their _ _ _ and instincts

12 This MLB team's manager is known for his aggressive baserunning tactics, including the occasional double steal

13 A well-executed double steal can shift the momentum of a game in favor of the offensive team, putting pressure on the _ _ _ team's pitcher and defense

14 This MLB player, known for his aggressive baserunning, has recorded multiple successful double steals throughout his career: Billy _ _ _

DOWN

1 In a double steal situation, the baserunners often rely on a _ _ _ signal from the third base coach to coordinate their timing

2 The double steal is often used as a strategic _ _ _ to generate scoring opportunities and put pressure on the opposing team's defense

4 A double steal can be a result of a _ _ _ throw by the catcher or a slow reaction by the infielders, allowing the baserunners to advance safely

5 A double steal occurs when two baserunners successfully advance to the next _ _ _ on the same play

8 The double steal is a high-risk, high-reward play that requires precise timing and quick _ _ _ by the baserunners

9 The double steal is an example of a team's willingness to take _ _ _ and be aggressive on the basepaths, even in high-pressure situations

78- Balk Call

ACROSS

2 A balk call can be a result of a pitcher trying to deceive _ _ _ baserunners with a quick pickoff attempt or feigned pitch delivery

3 This MLB team's fans are known for their loud boos and jeers when an opposing pitcher gets called for a balk, often trying to rattle them further

7 This MLB team's manager is known for his frustration with balk calls and often argues vehemently with umpires when they occur

8 This MLB pitcher is known for his quick delivery to the plate, but occasionally gets called for a balk due to his deceptive movements: Johnny _ _ _

9 This MLB manager, known for his emphasis on pitching fundamentals, often works with his pitchers to avoid balk calls and maintain proper mechanics: Bob _ _ _

10 This MLB pitcher, known for his unorthodox delivery, has been called for numerous balks throughout his career, leading to criticism from opposing teams: _ _ _ Fernandez

11 The balk call is often controversial, with some pitchers and managers arguing that it is a subjective _ _ _ and difficult to enforce consistently

12 This MLB team's fans are known for their "balk busters" chants, encouraging their team's pitchers to avoid costly balk calls with their precise movements

14 A balk call occurs when a pitcher makes an illegal _ _ _ movement while on the mound, resulting in a penalty for the defensive team

DOWN

1 A balk call can be a result of a pitcher making an abrupt _ _ _ motion or flinching while on the mound, leading to confusion among the umpires and players

4 A balk call can be particularly costly in close games, as it can result in _ _ _ baserunners or even runs scoring for the offensive team

5 This MLB pitcher, known for hi fiery demeanor on the mound, ha been ejected from games multipl times after arguing balk calls wit umpires: Max _ _ _

6 A balk call can be a result of a pitcher attempting to _ _ _ a baserunner by starting and stopping their delivery multiple times before finally pitching

9 This MLB pitcher, known for h meticulous attention to detail, rarely gets called for balks due t his precise movements on the mound

13 balk call can be a result of a pitcher failing to come to a complete stop in the _ _ _ positi before delivering the pitch

79- Hit by Pitch

ACROSS

2 This MLB manager, known for his emphasis on player safety, often advocates for stricter penalties for pitchers who hit batters with pitches

4 A hit by pitch can be a result of a pitcher ___ up on the mound or failing to properly execute their pitch delivery, leading to errant throws

7 A hit by pitch occurs when a pitcher's throw strikes a batter, resulting in the batter being awarded ___

9 This historic MLB ballpark, known for its ivy-covered outfield walls, has seen many hit by pitch incidents over the years: ___ Field

10 This MLB team's historic ballpark, located in St. Louis, has seen its fair share of hit by pitch incidents over the years: ___ Stadium

11 This MLB player, known for his ability to get on base, has been hit by numerous pitches throughout his career, often using his ___ to avoid serious injury: Chase ___

12 This MLB pitcher is notorious for his wild pitches and has hit numerous batters with errant throws: Aroldis ___

14 This MLB pitcher, known for his intimidating presence on the mound, has led the league in hit by pitches multiple times throughout his career: Randy ___

DOWN

1 A hit by pitch can be particularly ___ in close games, as it puts a baserunner on with no outs and can lead to scoring opportunities for the offensive team

3 In a hit by pitch situation, the batter is awarded first base and the play is recorded as a ___ ball

5 This MLB team's fans are known for their loud boos and jeers when one of their players gets hit by a pitch, often directing their anger toward the opposing teams: Philadelphia ___

6 A hit by pitch can be a result of a batter ___ the plate, making it difficult for the pitcher to find the strike zone and leading to wayward pitches

8 A hit by pitch can be a result of a pitcher trying to ___ the batter off the plate or retaliate for perceived infractions, leading to tension between teams

13 This MLB team's manager is known for his fiery demeanor and has been involved in heated arguments with umpires over hit by pitch calls

80- Fielder's Choice

ACROSS

3 A fielder's choice occurs when a batter reaches base safely due to the defensive team choosing to _ _ _ a different baserunner instead

4 This MLB player, known for his power hitting and aggressive baserunning, has recorded many fielder's choice situations throughout his career, often forcing defensive teams into difficult _ _ _

6 A fielder's choice can be a result of a batter hitting a sharp grounder or _ _ _ line drive that forces the defensive team to make quick decisions

9 This MLB player, known for his speed on the basepaths, has been involved in many fielder's choice situations, often putting pressure on opposing defenses with his aggressive baserunning: Dee _ _ _

12 A fielder's choice can be a result of a baserunner trying to advance on a _ _ _ fly ball or a ground ball hit to the infield, forcing the defense to make quick decisions

13 This MLB player is known for his ability to hit with power and consistency, often putting pressure on opposing defenses and leading to frequent fielder's choice situations

DOWN

1 The fielder's choice is often used as a strategic _ _ _ to advance baserunners and create scoring opportunities, especially in close games

2 In a fielder's choice situation, the defensive team often has to make quick _ _ _ to decide which baserunner to try to get out and where to throw the ball

4 This MLB team's fans are known for their "fielder's choice frenzy" celebrations, cheering loudly after a successful defensive play to get a baserunner out.

5 This MLB team's fans are known for their loud cheers and chants after a successful fielder's choice play, often appreciating the defensive effort involved

7 A fielder's choice can be a result of a _ _ _ throw by the defensive player, allowing the batter to reach base safely despite the attempt to get them out

8 This MLB player, known for his versatility and defensive prowess, has been involved in many memorable fielder's choice plays throughout his career: Ben _ _ _

10 This MLB team's manager is known for his aggressive baserunning tactics, often leading to numerous fielder's choice situations and putting pressure on opposing defenses

11 A fielder's choice can be particularly challenging for the defensive team in _ _ _ situations, when every out is crucial to the outcome of the game

81- Infield Fly

ACROSS

1 This MLB team's manager is known for his emphasis on defensive positioning, often instructing his infielders on how to handle infield fly situations

4 An infield fly is considered an automatic out, regardless of whether the ball is caught by a fielder or _ _ _ to the ground

8 In an infield fly situation, the umpire will signal by raising one _ _ _ and calling "infield fly" to alert the players and fans

9 This MLB team's fans are known for their loud cheers and chants when their team executes a successful infield fly play, often appreciating the defensive effort involved

10 This MLB player, known for his speed and aggressive baserunning, has been involved in many infield fly situations throughout his career, often putting pressure on the defensive team with his quick _ _ _

12 This MLB player, known for his versatility and defensive skills, has been involved in many infield fly situations throughout his career, often making critical catches to help his team: Ben _ _ _

14 An infield fly is intended to prevent the _ _ _ team from intentionally dropping the ball to create a force out or double play

15 The infield fly rule is designed to _ _ _ the offensive team from being unfairly penalized by a deliberate defensive tactic

DOWN

2 This MLB team's fans are known for their "infield fly fever" celebrations, cheering loudly after a successful defensive play to get the batter out

3 This MLB manager, known for his strategic acumen, often incorporates infield fly situations into his team's defensive game plan: Tony _ _ _

5 This MLB player is known for his defensive prowess in the infield, often catching infield fly balls with ease: Ozzie _ _ _

6 A successful infield fly requires quick decision-making and communication among the infielders, as well as _ _ _ in fielding the ball cleanly

7 An infield fly occurs when a fair fly ball is hit, and in the umpire's judgment, can be caught by an infielder with ordinary effort when first and second, or first, second, and third base are _ _ _ occupied

11 This historic MLB ballpark, located in Atlanta, has seen many memorable infield fly situations over the years, including a controversial one involving Chipper Jones in a playoff game: _ _ _ Park

13 This MLB player, known for his consistent performance at the plate and in the field, rarely gets called out on infield fly situations due to his excellent judgment

82- Fans Fever

ACROSS

1 These fervent supporters don red attire to show their allegiance to a team from Missouri

5 Fans of this team show their spirit by performing the "Tomahawk Chop" for a team from Georgia

6 The "Steel City" is home to fans of this MLB team

8 Fans of this team proudly wear red and white while rooting for a team from Ohio

10 The "Green Monster" stands tall behind the passionate fans of a team from Massachusetts

12 Fans of this team, known as the "Halos," cheer for a team from California

14 These die-hard followers wave the team's flag, chanting "Let's go, Royals!" for a team from Missouri

15 Known for their fervent support, fans of this MLB team are affectionately called "The Bleacher Creatures"

16 The "Philly Phanatic" entertains spirited fans of a team from the City of Brotherly Love

DOWN

2 The "Rockpile" rocks with the cheers of fans supporting a team from Colorado

3 The "Tribe" draws support from the loyal fans of a team from Ohio

4 Fans of this team, known as the "Motor City Kitties," cheer for a team from Michigan

5 The "Cheeseheads" are as famous as the team they support, a team from Wisconsin

7 Fans of this team proudly display the "C" flag while cheering for a team from the Windy City

9 "Dodger Blue" is synonymous with the dedicated fans of a team from Southern California

11 "Birdland" echoes with the cheers of enthusiastic fans of a team from Maryland

13 These fans, often seen with foam fingers and face paint, cheer on a team from the Bay Area

83- Famous Mascots

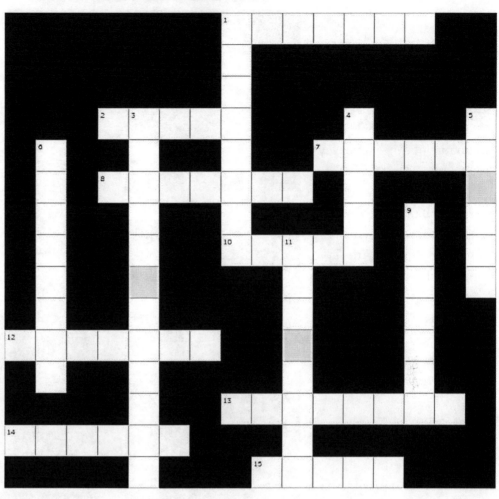

ACROSS

1 This racing condiment is a fan favorite at games played by the Milwaukee Brewers

2 The mascot of the Houston Astros who celebrates home runs with a train ride

7 This red bird is the mascot of the Arizona Diamondbacks

8 This energetic bird represents the Atlanta Braves

10 This furry green monster is an iconic figure at Fenway Park

12 The mustachioed mascot of the Pittsburgh Pirates who loves to entertain fans

13 The energetic bird who represents the St. Louis Cardinals

14 This large purple dinosaur is a beloved figure at Coors Field

15 A bear who brings joy to fans of the Chicago Cubs

DOWN

1 The energetic mascot of the Chicago White Sox who leads the team in cheers

3 A lovable elephant who cheers on fans of the Los Angeles Angels

4 This furry green monster is a beloved figure at games played by the Boston Red Sox

5 The orange-haired, mustachioed mascot of the New York Mets

6 The lovable green creature who entertains fans at games played by the Philadelphia Phillies

9 A green creature known for his mischievous antics at games played by the Oakland Athletics

11 The furry friend of the San Francisco Giants who wears a backward cap

84- Iconic Nicknames

ACROSS

3 This Hall of Fame pitcher was nicknamed "The Big Unit" due to his imposing stature: Randy _ _ _

7 "The Yankee Clipper" is the nickname of this iconic New York Yankees outfielder: Joe _ _ _

9 This MLB pitcher, known as "The Freak," earned two Cy Young Awards with the San Francisco Giants: Tim _ _ _

11 Known as "The Wizard," this Hall of Fame shortstop dazzled fans with his defensive prowess: Ozzie _ _ _

14 This MLB outfielder earned the nickname "The Kid" for his youthful exuberance and prodigious talent: Ken _ _ _

15 This MLB pitcher earned the nickname "Big Train" for his dominating performances on the mound: _ _ _ Johnson

16 This MLB pitcher earned the nickname "The Rocket" for his powerful fastball: Roger _ _ _

17 Known as "The Sultan of Swat," this legendary player set numerous home run records

DOWN

1 Known as "Pudge," this Hall of Fame catcher won multiple Gold Glove Awards during his career: Ivan _ _ _

2 "The Iron Horse" is the nickname of this legendary New York Yankees first baseman

4 This MLB outfielder, known as "The Splendid Splinter," was the last player to hit .400 in a season: Ted _ _ _

5 This MLB pitcher earned the nickname "Doc" for his dominant performances on the mound: Dwight _ _ _

6 "Mr. November" is the moniker given to this iconic New York Yankees shortstop

8 Known as "The Crime Dog," this MLB first baseman hit over 400 career home runs: Fred _ _ _

10 Known as "Charlie Hustle," this player holds the MLB record for career hits

12 "The Georgia Peach" is the nickname of this Hall of Fame outfielder who spent most of his career with the Detroit Tigers

13 This MLB outfielder, nicknamed "The Say Hey Kid," played most of his career for the New York/San Francisco Giants: Willie _ _ _

85- Baseball Lingo

ACROSS

5 A term used when a pitcher throws a strike that the batter swings at and misses

6 A pitch that is thrown with the intent of being difficult for the batter to hit: ___ Pitch

9 A term used when a pitcher throws a ball outside the strike zone

10 Achieved by a batter who makes contact with the ball and reaches base safely

DOWN

1 The area within the outfield fence where home runs are hit": Home Run ___

2 When a fielder catches a batted ball before it hits the ground

3 Refers to a batter who hits the ball into fair territory and is safe at first base

4 Describes a pitch that breaks downward sharply as it approaches the plate

7 A play where the batter makes contact with the ball, resulting in an out

8 A hit that reaches the outfield and allows the batter to advance to second base

86- Baseball Superstitions

ACROSS

2 A practice where players avoid stepping on this specific line to avoid bad luck: _ _ _ Line

5 A superstition where players avoid discussing a perfect game in progress to prevent jinxing it: _ _ _ Jinx

6 A ritual performed by players before games to bring luck to the team: _ _ _ Ritual

9 A practice where players perform a specific action or routine before each at-bat for good luck: _ _ _ Ritual

10 An often-observed practice where players avoid washing their uniform during a winning streak: _ _ _ Uniform

DOWN

1 A superstition that involves avoiding mentioning a no-hitter in progress to prevent jinxing it: _ _ _ Jinx

3 A widely-held belief that wearing a specific item or uniform in a certain way brings good luck: Lucky _ _ _

4 A superstition where players avoid mentioning a specific occurrence during a game to avoid jinxing it: _ _ _ Rule

7 A belief that certain items, such as hats or socks, must be worn in a specific way for luck: Lucky _ _ _

8 A common superstition involving touching a specific object or area for good luck before entering the field: Touching The _ _ _

87- Diving Catch

ACROSS

1 This MLB manager, known for his emphasis on defense, often praises his players for their diving catches and defensive contributions: Joe _ _ _

6 This MLB team's fans are known for their "diving catch dance" celebrations, where they mimic the motions of a fielder making a diving catch after a spectacular play

7 This MLB outfielder, known for his speed and agility, has a reputation for making diving catches look easy

13 The diving catch is often considered one of the most _ _ _ plays in baseball, showcasing the athleticism and skill of the fielder

DOWN

2 A diving catch can be a result of a _ _ _ effort by the fielder, sacrificing their body to make a play on a difficult ball.

3 In a diving catch situation, fielders often rely on their _ _ _ instincts and quick reflexes to make the play

4 This MLB coach, known for his expertise in outfield defense, often works with players to improve their diving catch technique and positioning: Ron _ _ _

5 This MLB outfielder, known for his acrobatic catches, has earned multiple Gold Glove Awards for his defensive prowess: Kevin _ _ _

8 A diving catch occurs when a fielder _ _ _ themselves to the ground to make a play on a batted ball.

9 This MLB team's fans are known for their loud cheers and applause after a player makes a diving catch, showing appreciation for their defensive efforts

10 This MLB team's historic ballpark, located in Pittsburgh, has seen many memorable diving catches over the years: _ _ _ Park

11 A diving catch can be a game-saving play, preventing runs from scoring and preserving a _ _ _ for the defensive team

12 This MLB player, known for his versatility and athleticism, has made numerous diving catches while playing multiple positions: Javier _ _ _

88- Pickoff Attempt

ACROSS

1 This MLB pitcher, known for his crafty pitching style, has developed an effective pickoff move that has fooled many baserunners

3 This MLB pitcher, known for his dominance on the mound, has recorded numerous successful pickoff attempts throughout his career: Clayton _ _ _

4 This MLB team's manager is known for his strategic use of pickoff attempts to control the running game

7 A successful pickoff attempt requires precise timing and a _ _ _ throw by the pitcher to catch the baserunner off guard

9 This MLB manager, known for his emphasis on fundamentals, often emphasizes the importance of pickoff attempts in preventing stolen bases

11 This MLB pitcher, known for his tall stature and deceptive delivery, has one of the best pickoff moves in the game: Jon _ _ _

12 This MLB team's fans are known for their loud cheers and applause after a successful pickoff attempt by their pitcher

13 In a pickoff attempt, the pitcher often uses a _ _ _ move to try to deceive the baserunner and make a successful throw to the base

DOWN

1 A pickoff attempt can be a result of a _ _ _ mistake by the baserunner, such as taking too big of a lead or being slow to react to the pitcher's move

2 This MLB team's fans are known for their elaborate celebrations after a successful pickoff attempt, often involving coordinated cheers and chants

5 A well-timed pickoff attempt can catch a baserunner _ _ _ and lead to an easy out

6 The pickoff attempt is an effective way for pitchers to _ _ _ the running game and prevent stolen bases

8 A pickoff attempt occurs when pitcher throws the ball to a _ _ _ in an attempt to catch a baserunner off the base

10 This MLB pitcher is known for his deceptive pickoff attempts, often catching baserunners off guard: Andy _ _ _

89- Tag Play

ACROSS

2 This MLB team's manager is known for his emphasis on fundamental baseball, including teaching his players proper techniques for tag plays

6 A tag play can be a result of a _ _ _ throw by the fielder, allowing them to apply the tag quickly and efficiently

9 This MLB team's fans are known for their loud cheers and applause after a successful tag play by their defensive players

10 This MLB catcher is known for his quick tags on tag plays, often preventing runners from scoring

11 This MLB team's historic ballpark, located in New York, has seen many memorable tag plays over the years: _ _ _ Stadium

14 A well-executed tag play requires _ _ _ timing and positioning by the fielder to apply the tag before the runner reaches the base.

15 This MLB player, known for his speed on the basepaths, has been involved in many close tag play situations during his career: Billy _ _ _

DOWN

1 A successful tag play can be a game-changing moment, preventing runs from scoring and preserving a lead for the _ _ _ team

3 A successful tag play requires quick _ _ _ and decision-making by the fielder, as well as effective communication with their teammates.

4 This MLB outfielder, known for his strong throwing arm, has assisted on many tag plays by making accurate throws to home plate: Mookie _ _ _

5 This historic MLB ballpark, located in Boston, has seen its fair share of memorable tag plays over the years

7 This MLB infielder, known for his defensive prowess, has recorded numerous successful tag plays throughout his career: Nolan _ _ _

8 A well-executed tag play can shift the momentum of the game in favor of the defensive team, preventing runs from _ _ _ and ending scoring threats

12 In a tag play situation, fielders often rely on their _ _ _ instincts and quick reflexes to make the tag before the runner reaches the base

13 A tag play occurs when a defensive player attempts to tag a baserunner with the ball to _ _ _ them out

90- Fair Ball

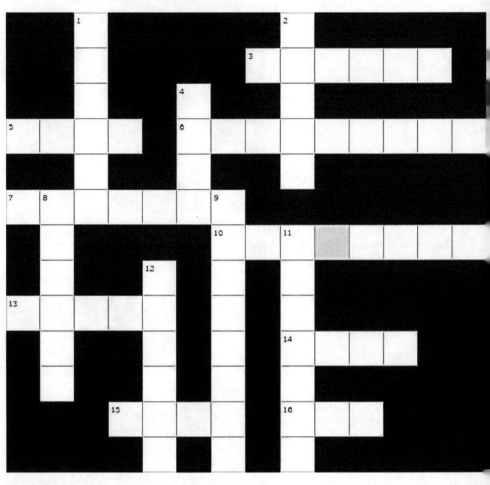

ACROSS

3 A fair ball is a batted ball that lands in the field of play and is not _ _ _ by a fielder before reaching the ground

5 This MLB team's fans are known for their loud cheers and applause after a fair ball is hit into play, anticipating potential _ _ _ and runs scored

6 The fair ball is a fundamental concept in baseball, determining the outcome of _ _ _ and defensive plays throughout the game

7 This MLB team's manager is known for his emphasis on hitting fundamentals, including teaching his players to make solid contact and hit fair balls

10 legendary player known for hitting towering home runs

13 This MLB player is known for his powerful swings, often hitting fair balls deep into the outfield: Aaron _ _ _

14 A well-placed fair ball can exploit defensive _ _ _ in the outfield and result in extra bases for the hitter

15 This MLB coach, known for his expertise in hitting mechanics, often works with players to improve their technique and consistency in hitting fair balls: Kevin _ _ _

16 A fair ball that is hit with power and precision can result in extra bases and _ _ _ scoring opportunities for the offensive team

DOWN

1 This MLB outfielder, known for his speed and agility, has a knack for tracking down fair balls hit into the gaps

2 A fair ball that lands in the outfield can result in extra _ _ _ for the offensive team, depending on the speed and positioning of the baserunners

4 A fair ball that travels over the outfield fence is called a _ _ _ run, resulting in an automatic score for the offensive team

8 This MLB player, known for his consistent contact hitting, has led the league in fair balls hit during multiple seasons

9 The fair ball is a fundamental element of the game, serving a the basis for offensive _ _ _ and scoring opportunities

11 This MLB team's fans are known for their elaborate celebrations after a fair ball is into the stands, often involving coordinated cheers and chants

12 This MLB pitcher, known for his dominant fastball, has induced many fair balls hit directly to infielders for easy o

SOLUTIONS

Puzzle #1

Puzzle #2

Puzzle #3

Puzzle #4

Puzzle #5

Puzzle #6

Puzzle #7

Puzzle #8

Puzzle #9

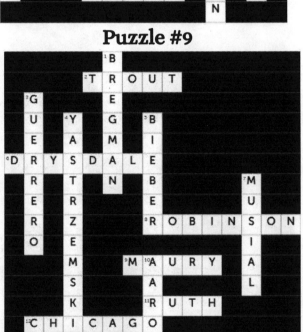

Puzzle #10

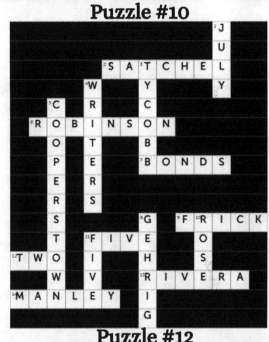

Puzzle #11

Puzzle #12

Puzzle #13

Puzzle #14

Puzzle #15

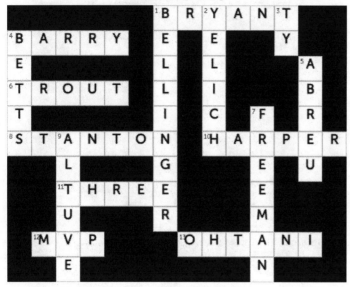

Puzzle #16

Puzzle #17

Puzzle #18

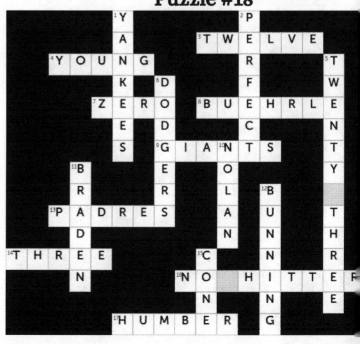

Puzzle #19

Puzzle #20

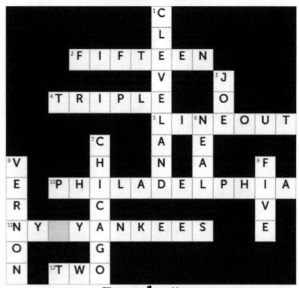

Puzzle #21

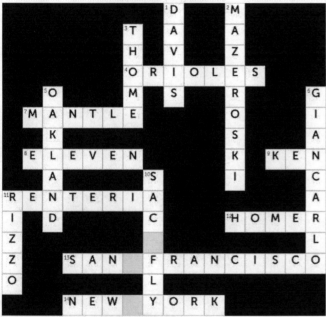

Puzzle #22

Puzzle #23

Puzzle #24

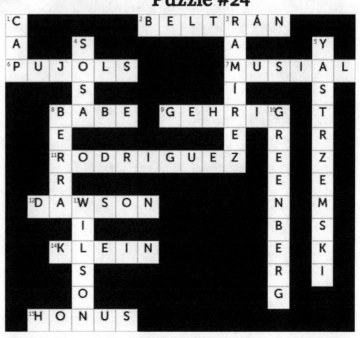

Puzzle #25

Puzzle #26

Puzzle #27

Puzzle #28

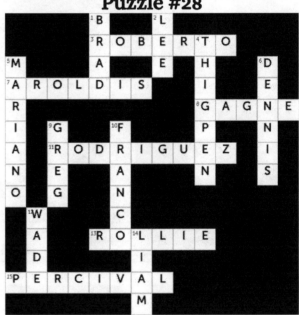

Puzzle #29

Puzzle #30

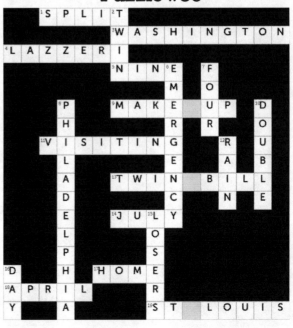

Puzzle #31

Puzzle #33

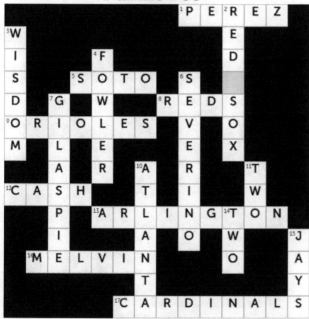

Puzzle #35

Puzzle #32

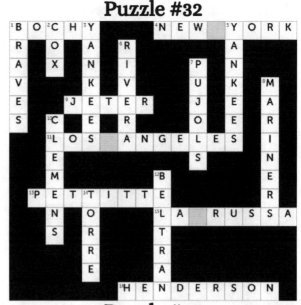

Puzzle #34

Puzzle #36

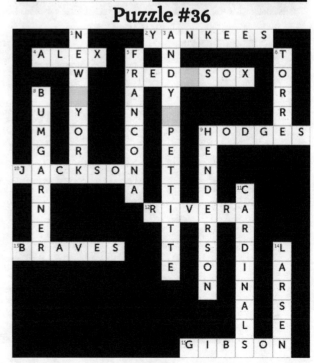

Puzzle #37

Puzzle #38

Puzzle #39

Puzzle #40

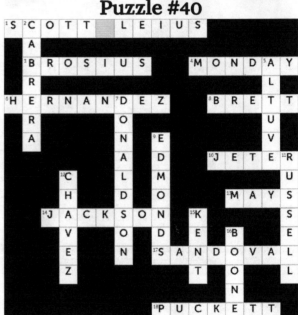

Puzzle #41

Puzzle #42

Puzzle #43

Puzzle #44

Puzzle #45

Puzzle #46

Puzzle #47

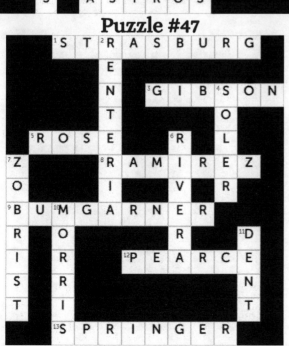

Puzzle #48

Puzzle #49

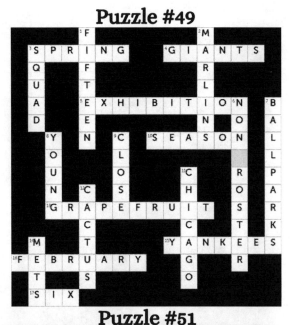

Puzzle #50

Puzzle #51

Puzzle #52

Puzzle #53

Puzzle #54

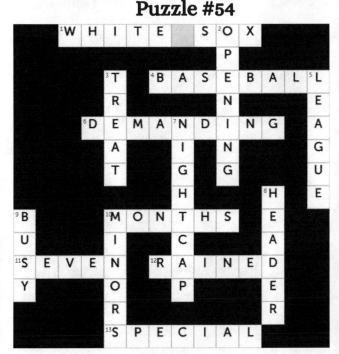

Puzzle #55

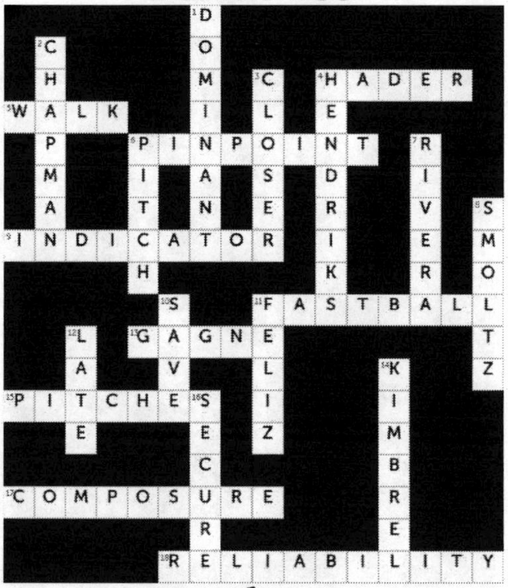

Puzzle #56

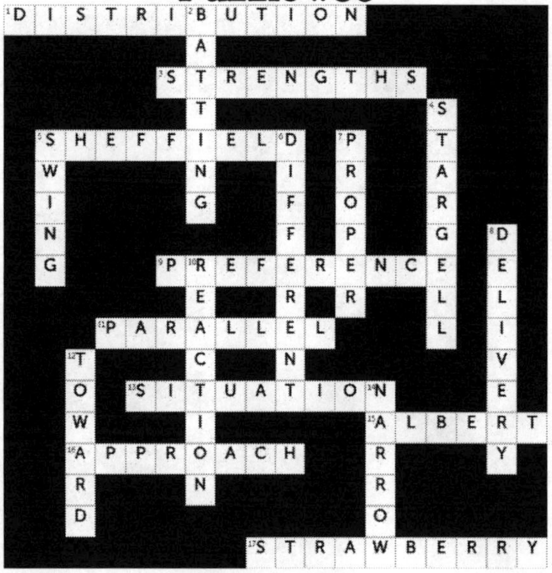

Puzzle #57

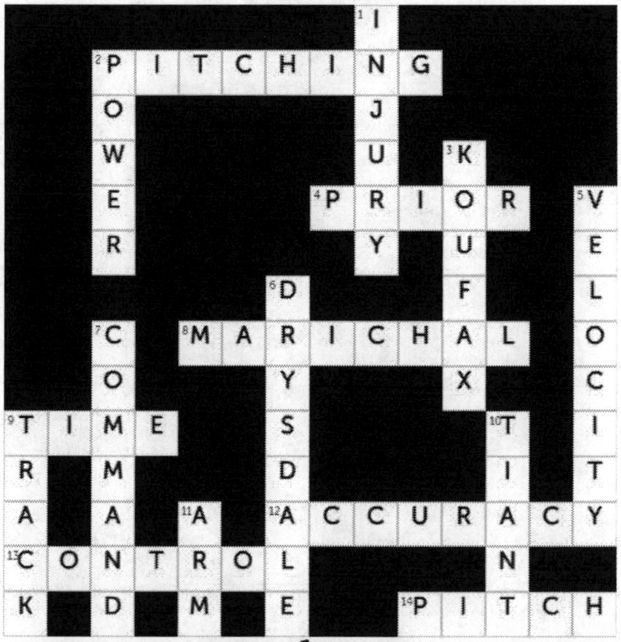

Puzzle #58

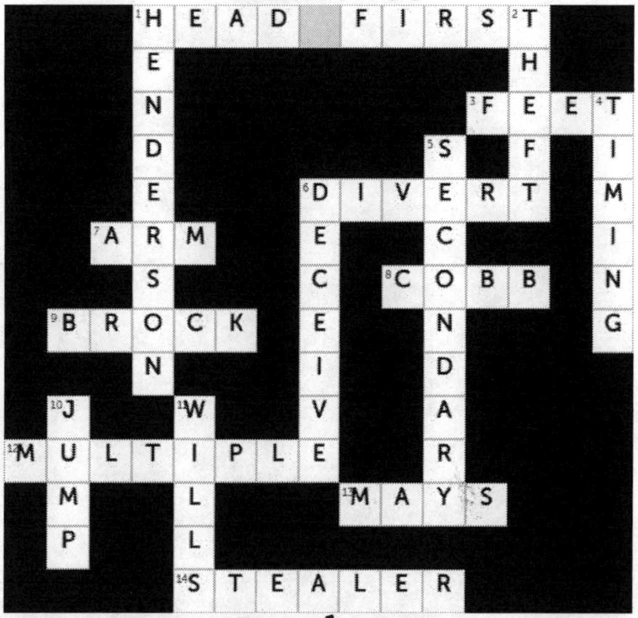

Puzzle #59

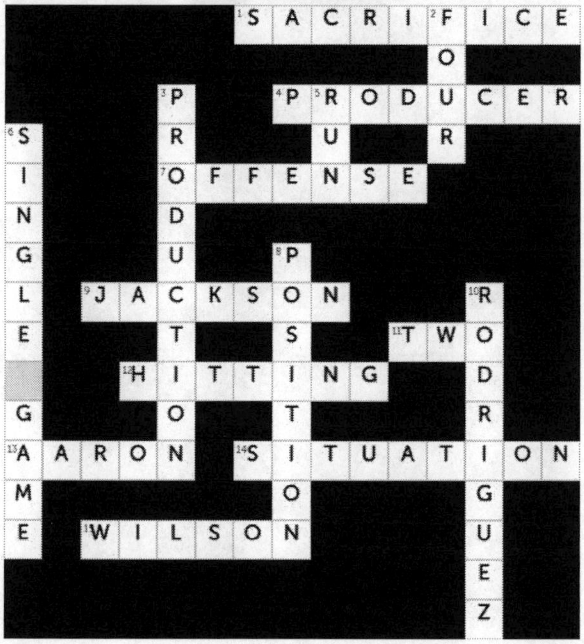

Puzzle #60

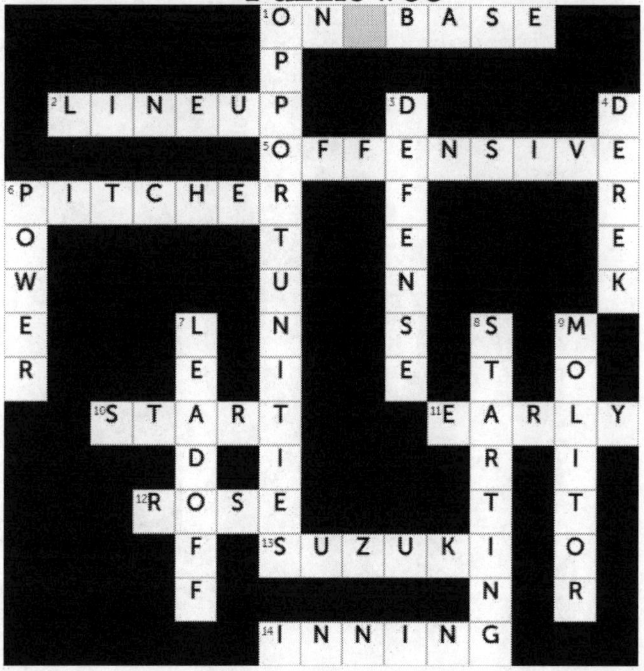

Puzzle #61

Puzzle #62

Puzzle #63

Puzzle #64

Puzzle #65

Puzzle #66

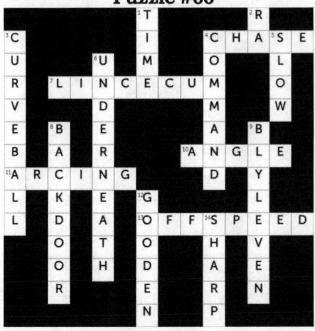

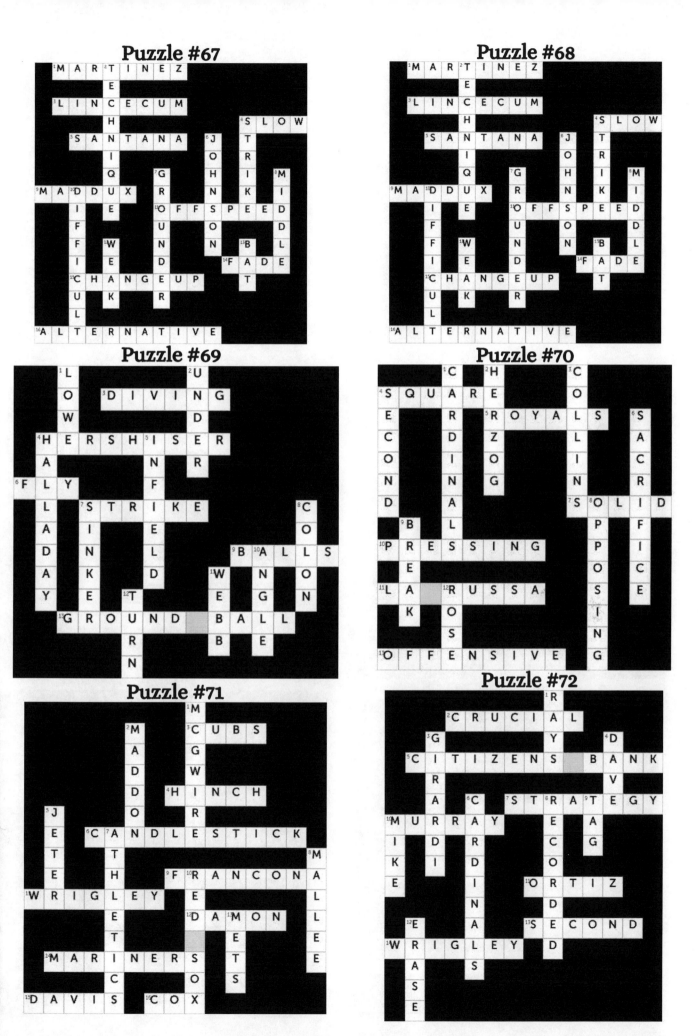

Puzzle #73

Across/Down answers visible in grid:
- BOND
- JOHN
- VOTTO
- FOUR / ROUND
- NIBBLE / GIANTS
- INNING
- CARDINAL
- YANKEES
- MIKE
- BASE / BJ
- DISCIPLINE
- CUBS
- RUNS

Puzzle #74

- HENDERSON
- JEFFERSON / STADT
- RO / BROCK
- DODGER
- ROBINSON
- BRAVES / JOE
- PITCH / LE
- SWING / FENWAY
- MADDON
- WHITE SOX
- ANTICIPATE

Puzzle #75

- DODGERS
- OPPORTUNIT
- ROOSTERT
- BASE
- TROUT / HENDERSON
- DEFENSIVE
- CRUCIAL / SUCCESS / SHARP
- ASTROS
- BILLY / JUMP / MET
- AREAS

Puzzle #76

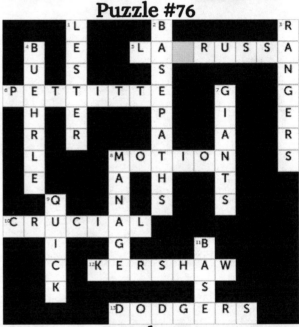

- LES / BASS / R
- BUSH / LA RUSSA / RANGERS
- PETTITTE / GIANTS
- PHRLEE / HERE / SPAANSHS
- MOTION
- MANAG
- QUICK
- CRUCIAL
- BS
- KERSHAW
- DODGERS

Puzzle #77

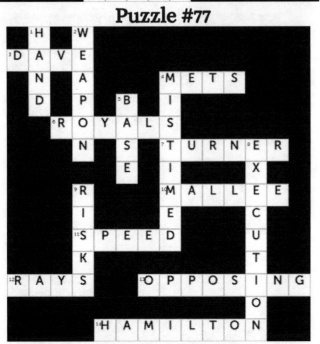

- H / W
- DAVE
- AND / WAAP
- METS
- MIS
- BA / SI
- ROYALS / ENS
- TURNER / EX
- RIK / MALLEE / ECUT
- SPEED
- K
- RAYS / OPPOSING
- HO
- HAMILTON

Puzzle #78

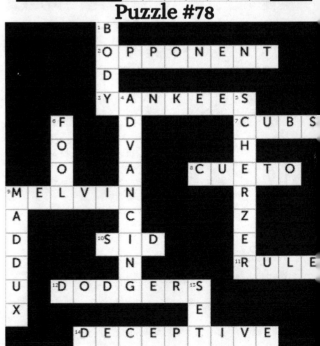

- B
- OPPONENT
- ODD
- YANKEES
- FOO / DVA / CUBS
- CHR
- CUETO
- MELVIN / RZ
- ADD / SID / E
- ADD / ON
- DUX / RULE
- DODGER / S
- DECEPTIVE

Puzzle #79

Puzzle #80

Puzzle #81

Puzzle #82

Puzzle #83

Puzzle #84

Puzzle #85

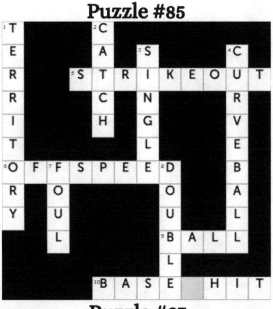

Puzzle #86

Puzzle #87

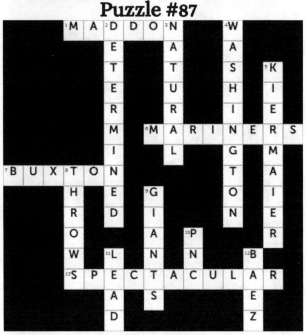

Puzzle #88

Puzzle #89

Puzzle #90

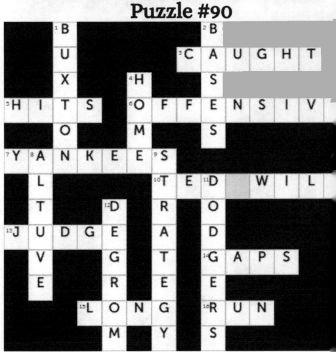

Made in the USA
Monee, IL
29 October 2024

68923286R00061